Thank you...

...for purchasing this copy of Homework Today for ages 7-8. We hope that you will find these 50 photocopiable worksheets helpful as part of your programme for homework activities. Each sheet is accompanied by an answer sheet. If you wish to, you can photocopy the answer sheets as well to enable your pupils to check their own work. Some sheets, of course, include questions where the answers will be completed in an individual way by the pupils.

Please note that photocopies can only be made for use by the purchasing institution; supplying copies to other schools, institutions or individuals breaches the copyright licence. Thank you for your help in this.

Overleaf we have drafted a letter which you may wish to photocopy, or amend, to send home to parents.

This Homework Today book is part of our growing range of educational titles. Most of our books are individual workbooks but, due to popular demand, we are now introducing a greater number of photocopiable titles especially for teachers. You may like to look out for:

Homework Today for ages 8-9
Homework Today for ages 9-10
Homework Today for ages 10-11
Numeracy Today for ages 5-7
Numeracy Today for ages 7-9
Numeracy Today for ages 9-11
Best Handwriting for ages 7-11
Spelling for Literacy (set of five books providing a complete spelling course for ages 5-11)

To find details of our other publications, please visit our website: www.acblack.com

Dear Parents,

We are pleased to be providing homework sheets for our seven to eight year old pupils, from a book called 'Homework Today'. These sheets contain activities which will enable your child to revise some of the skills and knowledge which they have acquired at school. The amount of time taken to complete each sheet will vary considerably but, as a guide, you should allow approximately 15 to 20 minutes per homework.

Try to help your child 'get into the homework habit' by providing a quiet place to work, with a desk or a table. Encourage your child to work in pen for written work and in pencil for maths. Neat presentation is important and reflects the pride your child takes in producing good quality work.

Thank you for supporting the work of the school by encouraging your child with homework.

Yours sincerely,

Homework Today is published by Andrew Brodie Publications.
Andrew Brodie Publications publish a range of educational workbooks for children,
available through bookstores or through the website: **www.acblack.com**

CONTENTS PAGE

Homework Today is published by Andrew Brodie Publications.
Andrew Brodie Publications publish a range of educational workbooks for children,
available through bookstores or through the website: **www.acblack.com**

Name: Date:

Fast Addition

Complete this addition square. We have started it for you.

+	1	2	3	4	5	6	7	8	9
1									
2							9		
3									
4				8					
5									
6									
7									16
8									
9									

Now try this one.

+	6	2	4	3	7	1	8	9	5
4									
3									
8									
5									
1									
6									
9									
7									
2									

Homework Today   **Answer Sheet**

Name: Date:

Fast Addition

Complete this addition square. We have started it for you.

+	1	2	3	4	5	6	7	8	9
1	2	3	4	5	6	7	8	9	10
2	3	4	5	6	7	8	9	10	11
3	4	5	6	7	8	9	10	11	12
4	5	6	7	8	9	10	11	12	13
5	6	7	8	9	10	11	12	13	14
6	7	8	9	10	11	12	13	14	15
7	8	9	10	11	12	13	14	15	16
8	9	10	11	12	13	14	15	16	17
9	10	11	12	13	14	15	16	17	18

+	6	2	4	3	7	1	8	9	5
4	10	6	8	7	11	5	12	13	9
3	9	5	7	6	10	4	11	12	8
8	14	10	12	11	15	9	16	17	13
5	11	7	9	8	12	6	13	14	10
1	7	3	5	4	8	2	9	10	6
6	12	8	10	9	13	7	14	15	11
9	15	11	13	12	16	10	17	18	14
7	13	9	11	10	14	8	15	16	12
2	8	4	6	5	9	3	10	11	7

Now try this one.

Homework Today

Name: Date:

Number Spellings

Copy the number word...

...then cover it and write it again.
Check your spelling!

Fold the paper
here to cover your word

Look carefully at the word.	Copy the word.	Write again, then check.
1 one		
2 two		
3 three		
4 four		
5 five		
6 six		
7 seven		
8 eight		
9 nine		
10 ten		
11 eleven		
12 twelve		
13 thirteen		
14 fourteen		
15 fifteen		
16 sixteen		
17 seventeen		
18 eighteen		
19 nineteen		
20 twenty		

Name: Date:

Number Spellings

Copy the number word...

...then cover it and write it again.
Check your spelling!

Fold the paper
here to cover your word

Look carefully at the word.	Copy the word.	Write again, then check.
1 one	one	one
2 two	two	two
3 three	three	three
4 four	four	four
5 five	five	five
6 six	six	six
7 seven	seven	seven
8 eight	eight	eight
9 nine	nine	nine
10 ten	ten	ten
11 eleven	eleven	eleven
12 twelve	twelve	twelve
13 thirteen	thirteen	thirteen
14 fourteen	fourteen	fourteen
15 fifteen	fifteen	fifteen
16 sixteen	sixteen	sixteen
17 seventeen	seventeen	seventeen
18 eighteen	eighteen	eighteen
19 nineteen	nineteen	nineteen
20 twenty	twenty	twenty

Name: Date:

More Number Spellings

Copy the number word, then cover it and write it again.
Don't forget to check your spellings!

Fold the paper
here to cover your word

Look carefully at the word.	Copy the word.	Write again, then check.
0 zero		
4 four		
14 fourteen		
40 forty		
30 thirty		
50 fifty		
60 sixty		
70 seventy		
80 eighty		
90 ninety		
100 hundred		
1000 thousand		
1000000 million		
1st first		
2nd second		
3rd third		
4th fourth		
5th fifth		
6th sixth		
7th seventh		

Name: Date:

More Number Spellings

Copy the number word, then cover it and write it again.
Don't forget to check your spellings!

Fold the paper
here to cover your word

Look carefully at the word.	Copy the word.	Write again, then check.
0 zero	zero	zero
4 four	four	four
14 fourteen	fourteen	fourteen
40 forty	forty	forty
30 thirty	thirty	thirty
50 fifty	fifty	fifty
60 sixty	sixty	sixty
70 seventy	seventy	seventy
80 eighty	eighty	eighty
90 ninety	ninety	ninety
100 hundred	hundred	hundred
1000 thousand	thousand	thousand
1000000 million	million	million
1st first	first	first
2nd second	second	second
3rd third	third	third
4th fourth	fourth	fourth
5th fifth	fifth	fifth
6th sixth	sixth	sixth
7th seventh	seventh	seventh

Odds and Evens

> Even numbers end in zero, two, four, six or eight.

Draw a ring around each even number:

17   2   48   300   29   74   201   94

> Odd numbers end in one, three, five, seven or nine.

Draw a ring around each odd number:

23   47   32   118   777   6   84   57

Answer the addition questions below. Write whether each number is odd or even. The first one is done for you.

6 + 4 = 10
↑   ↑   ↑
even   even   even

3 + 5 =
↑   ↑   ↑

7 + 2 =
↑   ↑   ↑

8 + 5 =
↑   ↑   ↑

9 + 8 =
↑   ↑   ↑

Fill in the missing words:

Even number + Even number = _____ number

Odd number + Odd number = _____ number

Even number + Odd number = _____ number

Odd number + Even number = _____ number

Name: Date:

Odds and Evens

Even numbers end in zero, two, four, six or eight.

Draw a ring around each even number:

17   (2)   (48)   (300)   29   (74)   201   (94)

Odd numbers end in one, three, five, seven or nine.

Draw a ring around each odd number:

(23)   (47)   32   118   (777)   6   84   (57)

Answer the addition questions below. Write whether each number is odd or even. The first one is done for you.

6 + 4 = | 10 |
↑   ↑   ↑
| even | even | | even |

3 + 5 = | 8 |
↑   ↑   ↑
| odd | odd | | even |

7 + 2 = | 9 |
↑   ↑   ↑
| odd | | even | | odd |

8 + 5 = | 13 |
↑   ↑   ↑
| even | | odd | | odd |

9 + 8 = | 17 |
↑   ↑   ↑
| odd | | even | | odd |

Fill in the missing words:

Even number + Even number = | even | number

Odd number + Odd number = | even | number

Even number + Odd number = | odd | number

Odd number + Even number = | odd | number

Words and Numbers

Join the numbers to the words. We've done one for you.

33   eighty-three

26   seven

114   sixty-nine

298   thirty-three

7   one hundred and eighty-three

83   two hundred and ninety-eight

183   one hundred and fourteen

69   two hundred and eighty-three

283   twenty-six

Now write the correct words for the numbers shown. Try to spell the words correctly.

64 →	
28 →	
144 →	
39 →	
516 →	
748 →	
99 →	
386 →	

Words and Numbers

Join the numbers to the words. We've done one for you.

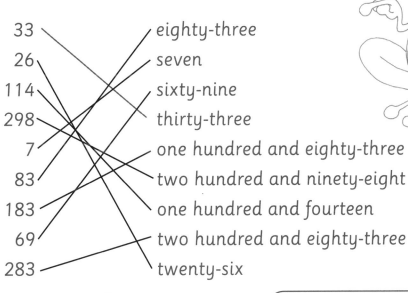

33	eighty-three
26	seven
114	sixty-nine
298	thirty-three
7	one hundred and eighty-three
83	two hundred and ninety-eight
183	one hundred and fourteen
69	two hundred and eighty-three
283	twenty-six

Now write the correct words for the numbers shown. Try to spell the words correctly.

64	→	sixty-four
28	→	twenty-eight
144	→	one hundred and forty-four
39	→	thirty-nine
516	→	five hundred and sixteen
748	→	seven hundred and forty-eight
99	→	ninety-nine
386	→	three hundred and eighty-six

Homework Today

Name: Date:

Additions to 20

We need to be able to
add numbers quickly.

Answer these as quickly as you can:

6 + 4 = ☐   7 + 2 = ☐   9 + 3 = ☐

8 + 5 = ☐   7 + 8 = ☐   6 + 9 = ☐

8 + 8 = ☐   9 + 9 = ☐   7 + 7 = ☐

Now try these:

4 + ☐ = 6   3 + ☐ = 10   ☐ + 8 = 14

5 + ☐ = 12   9 + ☐ = 17   ☐ + 6 = 12

☐ + 8 = 15   2 + ☐ = 15   5 + ☐ = 15

1 + 10 = 11   10 +1 = 11
2 + 9 = 11   9 +2 = 11
3 + 8 = 11   8 +3 = 11
4 + 7 = 11   7 +4 = 11
5 + 6 = 11   6 +5 = 11

Look at these ways of making eleven by
adding two whole numbers.

Choose numbers to make these additions work:

☐ + △ = 15   ☐ + △ = 12

☐ + △ = 19   ☐ + △ = 10

☐ + △ = 16   ☐ + △ = 14

☐ + △ = 18   ☐ + △ = 20

Name: Date:

Additions to 20

We need to be able
to add numbers quickly.

Answer these as quickly as you can:

6 + 4 = **10**   7 + 2 = **9**   9 + 3 = **12**

8 + 5 = **13**   7 + 8 = **15**   6 + 9 = **15**

8 + 8 = **16**   9 + 9 = **18**   7 + 7 = **14**

Now try these:

4 + **2** = 6   3 + **7** = 10   **6** + 8 = 14

5 + **7** = 12   9 + **8** = 17   **6** + 6 = 12

7 + 8 = 15   2 + **13** = 15   5 + **10** = 15

1 + 10 = 11   10 + 1 = 11
2 + 9 = 11   9 + 2 = 11
3 + 8 = 11   8 + 3 = 11
4 + 7 = 11   7 + 4 = 11
5 + 6 = 11   6 + 5 = 11

Look at these ways of making eleven by
adding two whole numbers.

Choose numbers to make these additions work:

9 + **6** = 15   **3** + **9** = 12

10 + **9** = 19   **5** + **5** = 10

12 + **4** = 16   **6** + **8** = 14

9 + **9** = 18   **15** + **5** = 20

Other
answers
are
possible.

Subtractions within 20

We need to be able to
subtract numbers quickly.

Answer these as quickly as you can:

8 – 2 = ☐   10 – 4 = ☐   12 – 5 = ☐

9 – 6 = ☐   12 – 4 = ☐   18 – 3 = ☐

16 – 7 = ☐   19 – 13 = ☐   14 – 8 = ☐

Now try these:

8 – ☐ = 6   9 – ☐ = 5   12 – ☐ = 8

15 – ☐ = 7   13 – ☐ = 8   17 – ☐ = 9

16 – ☐ = 12   18 – ☐ = 11   19 – ☐ = 13

13 – 1 = 12   17 – 5 = 12
14 – 2 = 12   18 – 6 = 12
15 – 3 = 12   19 – 7 = 12
16 – 4 = 12   20 – 8 = 12

Look at these ways of making twelve by
subtracting one whole number from another.

Find ways of making 9 by subtracting one whole number from another.
Use only numbers which are less than 21:

☐ 12 – 3

9

Name: _____   Date: _____

Subtractions within 20

We need to be able to subtract numbers quickly.

Answer these as quickly as you can:

8 – 2 = [6]   10 – 4 = [6]   12 – 5 = [7]

9 – 6 = [3]   12 – 4 = [8]   18 – 3 = [15]

16 – 7 = [9]   19 – 13 = [6]   14 – 8 = [6]

Now try these:

8 – [2] = 6   9 – [4] = 5   12 – [4] = 8

15 – [8] = 7   13 – [5] = 8   17 – [8] = 9

16 – [4] = 12   18 – [7] = 11   19 – [6] = 13

Look at these ways of making twelve by subtracting one whole number from another.

13 – 1 = 12   17 – 5 = 12
14 – 2 = 12   18 – 6 = 12
15 – 3 = 12   19 – 7 = 12
16 – 4 = 12   20 – 8 = 12

Find ways of making 9 by subtracting one whole number from another.
Use only numbers which are less than 21:

| 12 – 3 | | 18 – 9 |

| 17 – 8 | | 13 – 4 |

| 19 – 10 | | 16 – 7 |

9

| 15 – 6 | | 11 – 2 |

Other answers are possible.

Homework Today

Name: Date:

Multiplication Tables

Fill in the missing answers in these multiplication tables:

2 x table	
1 x 2 =	2
2 x 2 =	☐
3 x 2 =	6
4 x 2 =	☐
5 x 2 =	10
6 x 2 =	☐
7 x 2 =	☐
8 x 2 =	16
9 x 2 =	☐
10 x 2 =	20

3 x table	
1 x 3 =	3
2 x 3 =	6
3 x 3 =	☐
4 x 3 =	☐
5 x 3 =	15
6 x 3 =	☐
7 x 3 =	☐
8 x 3 =	24
9 x 3 =	☐
10 x 3 =	30

4 x table	
1 x 4 =	4
2 x 4 =	☐
3 x 4 =	☐
4 x 4 =	16
5 x 4 =	☐
6 x 4 =	24
7 x 4 =	☐
8 x 4 =	☐
9 x 4 =	☐
10 x 4 =	☐

5 x table	
1 x 5 =	5
2 x 5 =	☐
3 x 5 =	15
4 x 5 =	☐
5 x 5 =	☐
6 x 5 =	30
7 x 5 =	☐
8 x 5 =	☐
9 x 5 =	☐
10 x 5 =	☐

10 x table	
1 x 10 =	☐
2 x 10 =	☐
3 x 10 =	☐
4 x 10 =	☐
5 x 10 =	☐
6 x 10 =	☐
7 x 10 =	☐
8 x 10 =	☐
9 x 10 =	☐
10 x 10 =	☐

How quickly can you say the two times table without looking at it? Keep practising!

Name: Date:

Multiplication Tables

Fill in the missing answers in these multiplication tables:

2 x table

1 x 2 =   2
2 x 2 = | 4 |
3 x 2 =   6
4 x 2 = | 8 |
5 x 2 =   10
6 x 2 = | 12 |
7 x 2 = | 14 |
8 x 2 =   16
9 x 2 = | 18 |
10 x 2 =   20

3 x table

1 x 3 =   3
2 x 3 =   6
3 x 3 = | 9 |
4 x 3 = | 12 |
5 x 3 =   15
6 x 3 = | 18 |
7 x 3 = | 21 |
8 x 3 =   24
9 x 3 = | 27 |
10 x 3 =   30

4 x table

1 x 4 =   4
2 x 4 = | 8 |
3 x 4 = | 12 |
4 x 4 =   16
5 x 4 = | 20 |
6 x 4 =   24
7 x 4 = | 28 |
8 x 4 = | 32 |
9 x 4 = | 36 |
10 x 4 = | 40 |

5 x table

1 x 5 =   5
2 x 5 = | 10 |
3 x 5 =   15
4 x 5 = | 20 |
5 x 5 = | 25 |
6 x 5 =   30
7 x 5 = | 35 |
8 x 5 = | 40 |
9 x 5 = | 45 |
10 x 5 = | 50 |

10 x table

1 x 10 = | 10 |
2 x 10 = | 20 |
3 x 10 = | 30 |
4 x 10 = | 40 |
5 x 10 = | 50 |
6 x 10 = | 60 |
7 x 10 = | 70 |
8 x 10 = | 80 |
9 x 10 = | 90 |
10 x 10 = | 100 |

How quickly can you say the two times table without looking at it? Keep practising!

Homework Today

Name: Date:

Multiplication and Division

Use the five times table to help you to answer the division questions.

1 x 5 = 5
2 x 5 = 10
3 x 5 = 15
4 x 5 = 20
5 x 5 = 25
6 x 5 = 30
7 x 5 = 35
8 x 5 = 40
9 x 5 = 45
10 x 5 = 50

30 ÷ 5 =
15 ÷ 5 =
40 ÷ 5 = 8
20 ÷ 5 =
5 ÷ 5 =
35 ÷ 5 =
25 ÷ 5 =
50 ÷ 5 =
10 ÷ 5 =
45 ÷ 5 =

Now try these:

1 x 3 = 3	12 ÷ 3 =	1 x 4 = 4	16 ÷ 4 =
2 x 3 = 6	21 ÷ 3 =	2 x 4 = 8	12 ÷ 4 =
3 x 3 = 9	18 ÷ 3 =	3 x 4 = 12	32 ÷ 4 =
4 x 3 = 12	27 ÷ 3 =	4 x 4 = 16	8 ÷ 4 =
5 x 3 = 15	3 ÷ 3 =	5 x 4 = 20	28 ÷ 4 =
6 x 3 = 18	6 ÷ 3 =	6 x 4 = 24	4 ÷ 4 =
7 x 3 = 21	24 ÷ 3 =	7 x 4 = 28	36 ÷ 4 =
8 x 3 = 24	9 ÷ 3 =	8 x 4 = 32	20 ÷ 4 =
9 x 3 = 27	30 ÷ 3 =	9 x 4 = 36	40 ÷ 4 =
10 x 3 = 30	15 ÷ 3 =	10 x 4 = 40	24 ÷ 4 =

Name: Date:

Multiplication and Division

Use the five times table to help you to answer the division questions.

1 x 5 = 5	30 ÷ 5 = [6]
2 x 5 = 10	15 ÷ 5 = [3]
3 x 5 = 15	40 ÷ 5 = 8
4 x 5 = 20	20 ÷ 5 = [4]
5 x 5 = 25	5 ÷ 5 = [1]
6 x 5 = 30	35 ÷ 5 = [7]
7 x 5 = 35	25 ÷ 5 = [5]
8 x 5 = 40	50 ÷ 5 = [10]
9 x 5 = 45	10 ÷ 5 = [2]
10 x 5 = 50	45 ÷ 5 = [9]

Now try these:

1 x 3 = 3	12 ÷ 3 = [4]	1 x 4 = 4	16 ÷ 4 = [4]
2 x 3 = 6	21 ÷ 3 = [7]	2 x 4 = 8	12 ÷ 4 = [3]
3 x 3 = 9	18 ÷ 3 = [6]	3 x 4 = 12	32 ÷ 4 = [8]
4 x 3 = 12	27 ÷ 3 = [9]	4 x 4 = 16	8 ÷ 4 = [2]
5 x 3 = 15	3 ÷ 3 = [1]	5 x 4 = 20	28 ÷ 4 = [7]
6 x 3 = 18	6 ÷ 3 = [2]	6 x 4 = 24	4 ÷ 4 = [1]
7 x 3 = 21	24 ÷ 3 = [8]	7 x 4 = 28	36 ÷ 4 = [9]
8 x 3 = 24	9 ÷ 3 = [3]	8 x 4 = 32	20 ÷ 4 = [5]
9 x 3 = 27	30 ÷ 3 = [10]	9 x 4 = 36	40 ÷ 4 = [10]
10 x 3 = 30	15 ÷ 3 = [5]	10 x 4 = 40	24 ÷ 4 = [6]

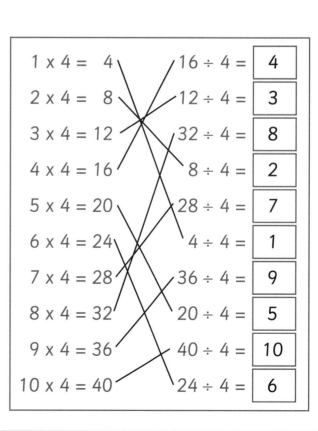

Reading Scales

What measurement is shown on each of the scales, to the nearest half kilogram?

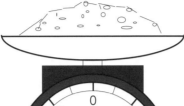

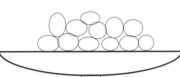

(a) [ ]

(b) [ ]

(c) [ ]

(d) [ ]

(e) [ ]

Draw pointers on these scales to show the measurements provided.

(f) $1\frac{1}{2}$ kg

(g) $5\frac{1}{2}$ kg

(h) $2\frac{1}{4}$ kg

Name: Date:

Reading Scales

What measurement is shown on each of the scales, to the nearest half kilogram?

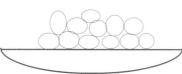

(a) $3\frac{1}{2}$ Kilograms

(b) 6 Kilograms

(c) 5 Kilograms

(d) $2\frac{1}{2}$ Kilograms

(e) $4\frac{1}{2}$ Kilograms

Draw pointers on these scales to show the measurements provided.

(f) $1\frac{1}{2}$ kg

(g) $5\frac{1}{2}$ kg

(h) $2\frac{1}{4}$ kg

Homework Today

Name: Date:

A Measuring Jug

Write the quantity shown in each measuring jug. Write your answers in millilitres (ml).

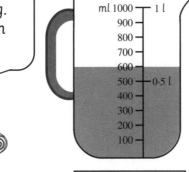

(a)

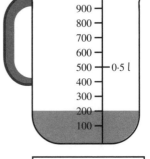

(b)

(c)

(d)

(e)

(f)

(g)

(h)

Name: Date:

A Measuring Jug

Write the quantity shown in each measuring jug. Write your answers in millilitres (ml).

(a) **600 ml**

(b) **200 ml**

(c) **750 ml**

(d) **450 ml**

(e) **900 ml**

(f) **500 ml**

(g) **700 ml**

(h) **1000 ml**

Number 12

Homework Today

Name: Date:

Clocks

This analogue clock shows half past two.
2:30
This digital clock shows half past two.

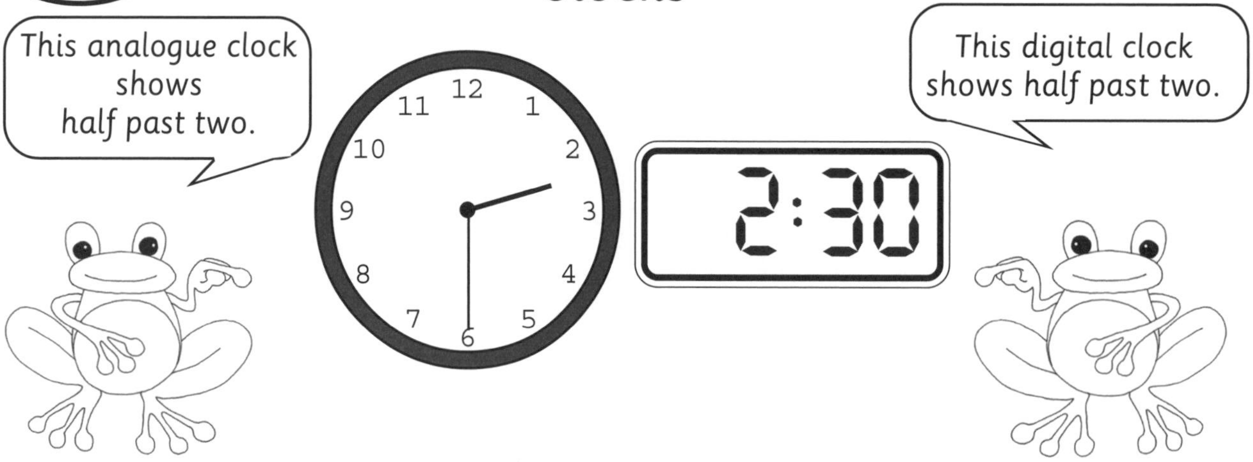

Fill in the missing information below:

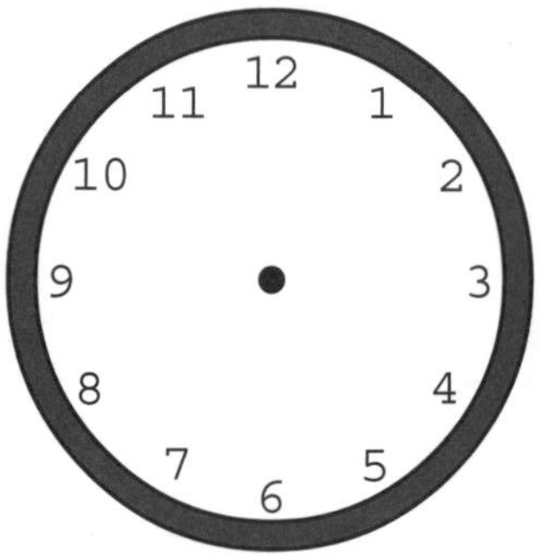

ten minutes past four

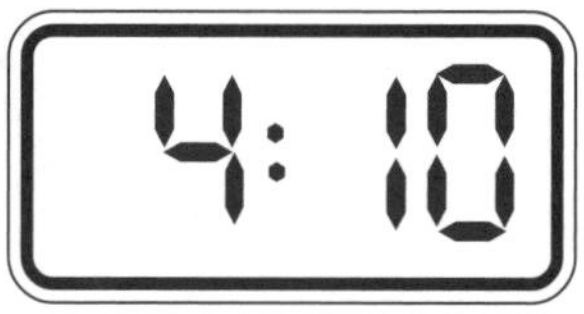

4: 10

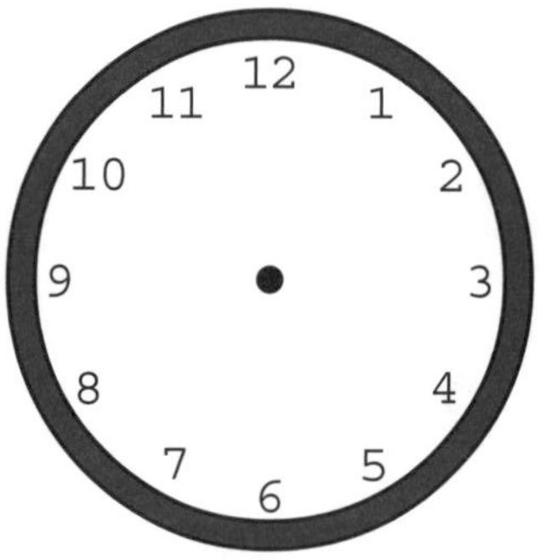

twenty minutes past eight

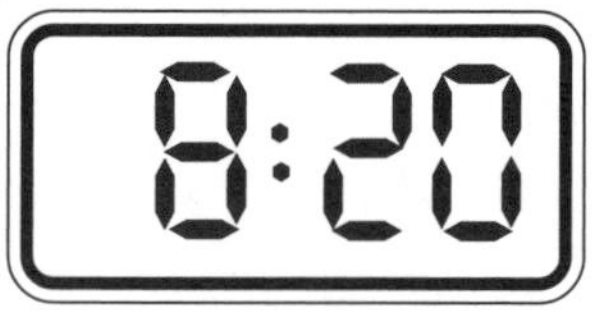

8:20

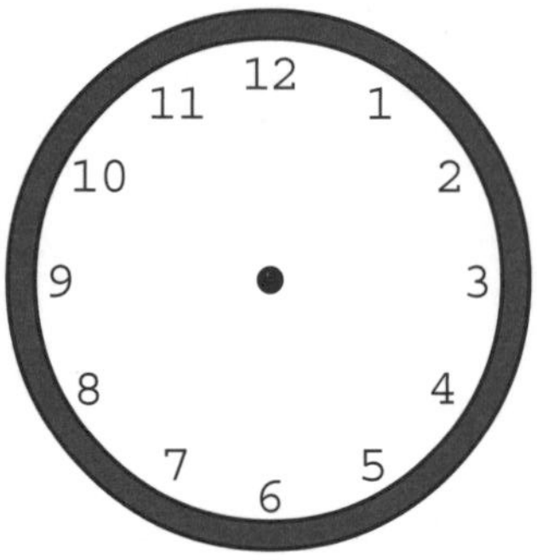

five minutes to seven

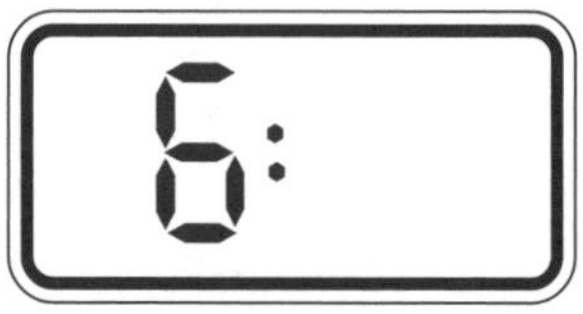

6:

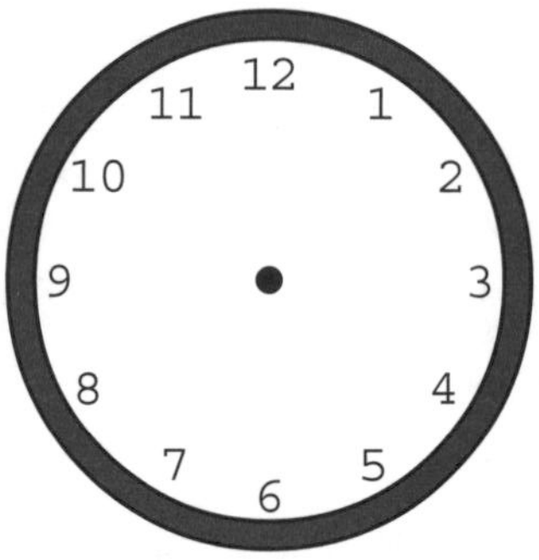

twenty-five minutes to two

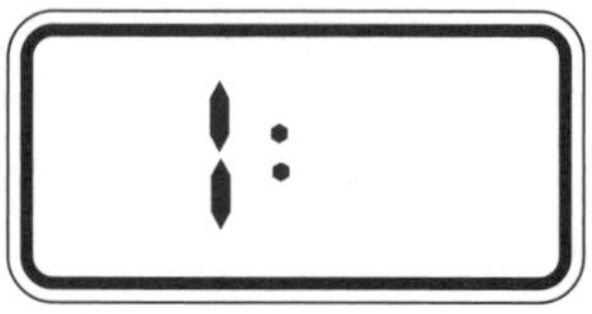

1:

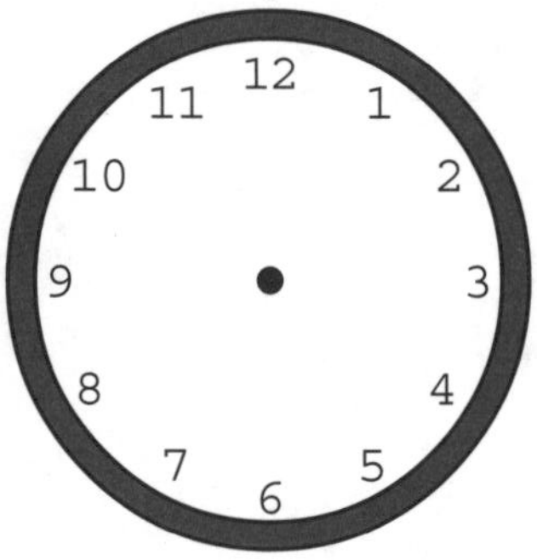

fifteen minutes past six

:

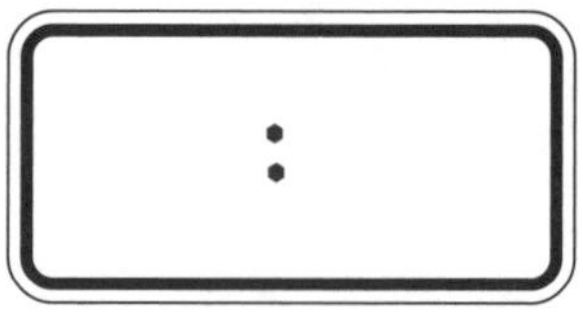

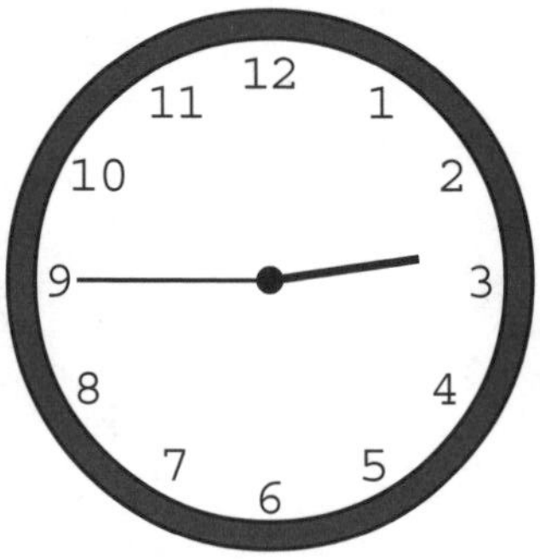

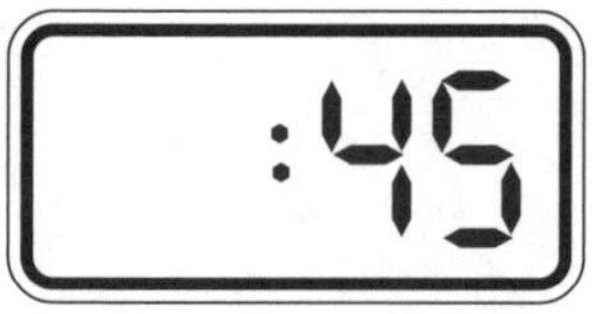

:45

On the back of the sheet, draw an analogue clock and a digital clock to show what the time is <u>now</u>.

Name: Date:

Clocks

This analogue clock shows half past two

This digital clock shows half past two.

Fill in the missing information below:

ten minutes past four

twenty minutes past eight

five minutes to seven

twenty-five minutes to two

fifteen minutes past six

fifteen minutes to three (quarter to three)

On the back of the sheet, draw an analogue clock and a digital clock to show what the time is <u>now</u>.

Homework Today

Name: Date:

Shapes

Write the correct name for each shape. Some names may be used more than once.

WORD BANK

circle   hexagon   octagon   pentagon
semicircle   rectangle   triangle   square

Homework Today   Answer Sheet

Number **13**

Name: Date:

Shapes

Write the correct name for each shape. Some names may be used more than once.

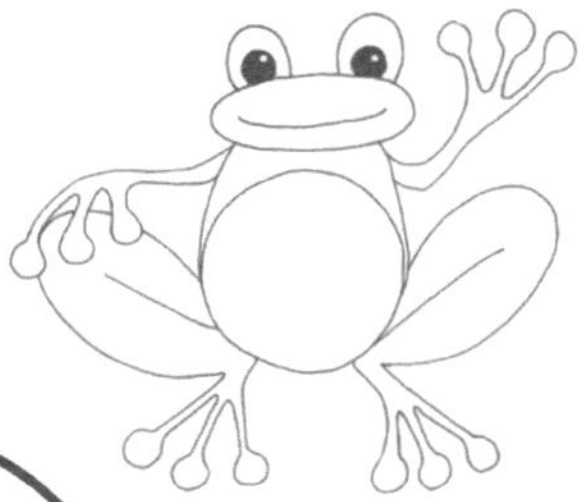

WORD BANK

circle   hexagon   octagon   pentagon
semicircle   rectangle   triangle   square

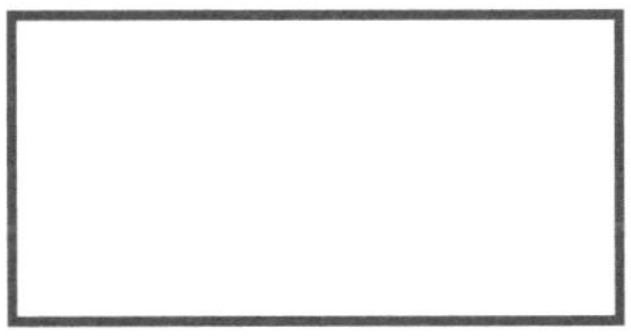

rectangle

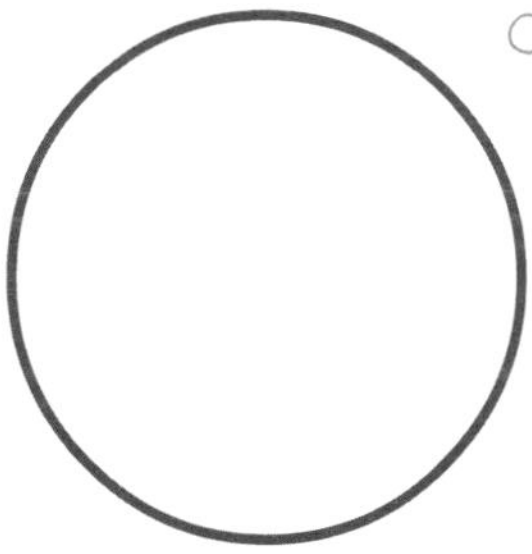

circle

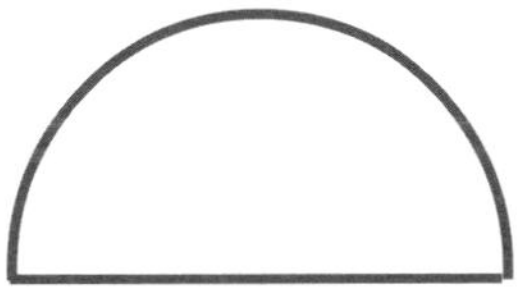

semicircle

square

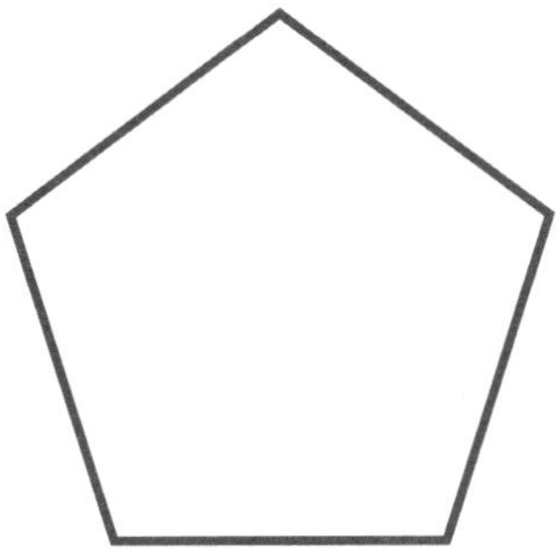

pentagon

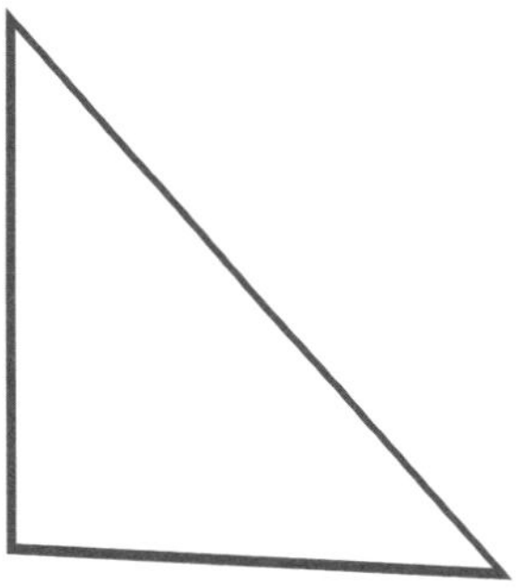

triangle

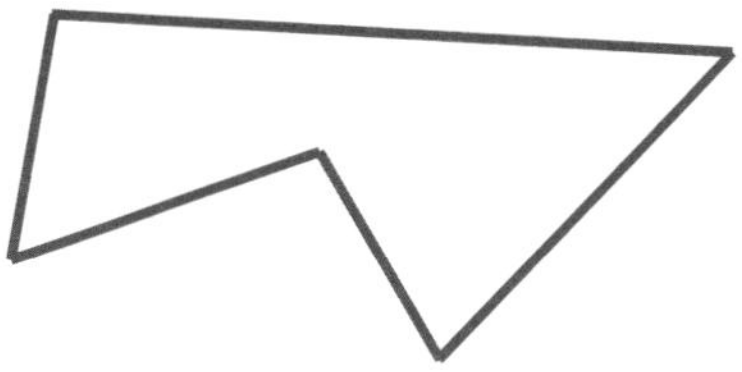

pentagon

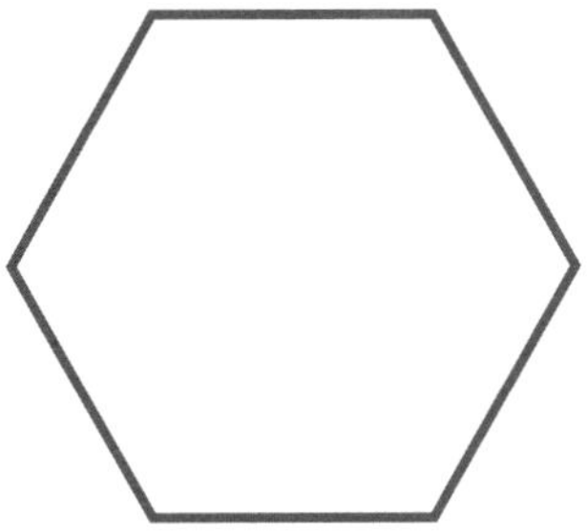

hexagon

rectangle

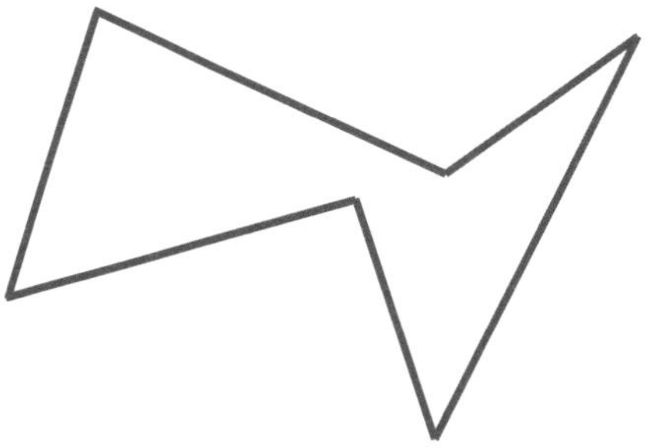

hexagon

Name: Date:

Squares on a Grid

Follow the instructions to draw a picture on the grid.

We have coloured square H12 for you.

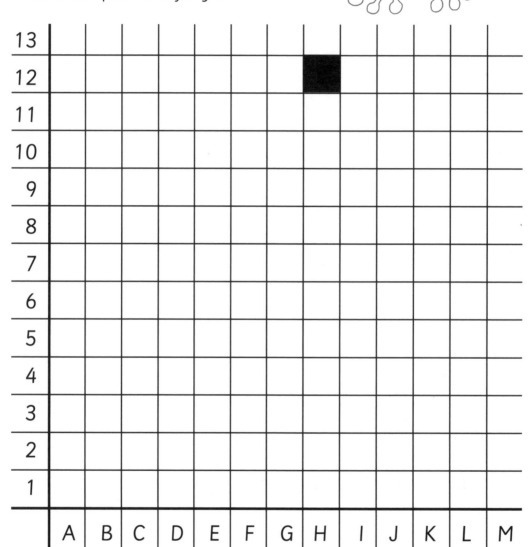

Colour square F12 black.
Colour squares F10, F11, G10, G11, H10 and H11 in dark green.
Colour squares E7, E8, E9, F7, F8, F9, G7, G8, G9, H7, H8, H9, I7, I8 and I9 in yellow.
Colour squares D9, C9, C10 and D11 in dark green.
Colour squares J9, K9, K10 and J11 in dark green.
Colour squares E6, D6, C5, D4, D3 and C3 in dark green.
Colour squares I6, J6, K5, J4, J3 and K3 in dark green.

Number
14

Name: Date:

Squares on a Grid

Follow the instructions to draw a picture on the grid.

We have coloured square H12 for you.

Colour square F12 black.
Colour squares F10, F11, G10, G11, H10 and H11 in dark green.
Colour squares E7, E8, E9, F7, F8, F9, G7, G8, G9, H7, H8, H9, I7, I8 and I9 in yellow.
Colour squares D9, C9, C10 and D11 in dark green.
Colour squares J9, K9, K10 and J11 in dark green.
Colour squares E6, D6, C5, D4, D3 and C3 in dark green.
Colour squares I6, J6, K5, J4, J3 and K3 in dark green.

Homework Today

Name: Date:

The Compass

Write the correct words in the boxes.
We have written North for you.

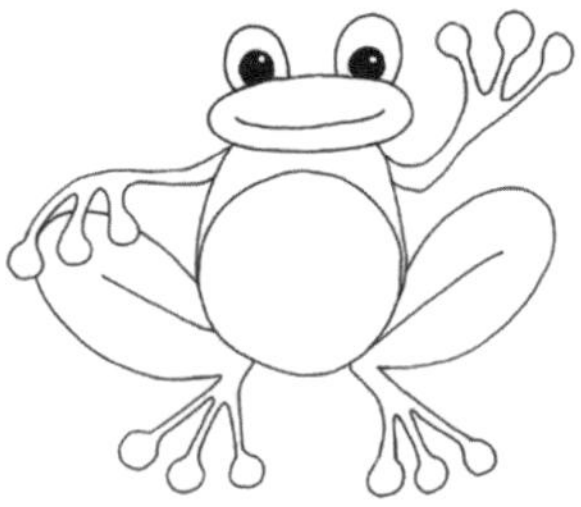

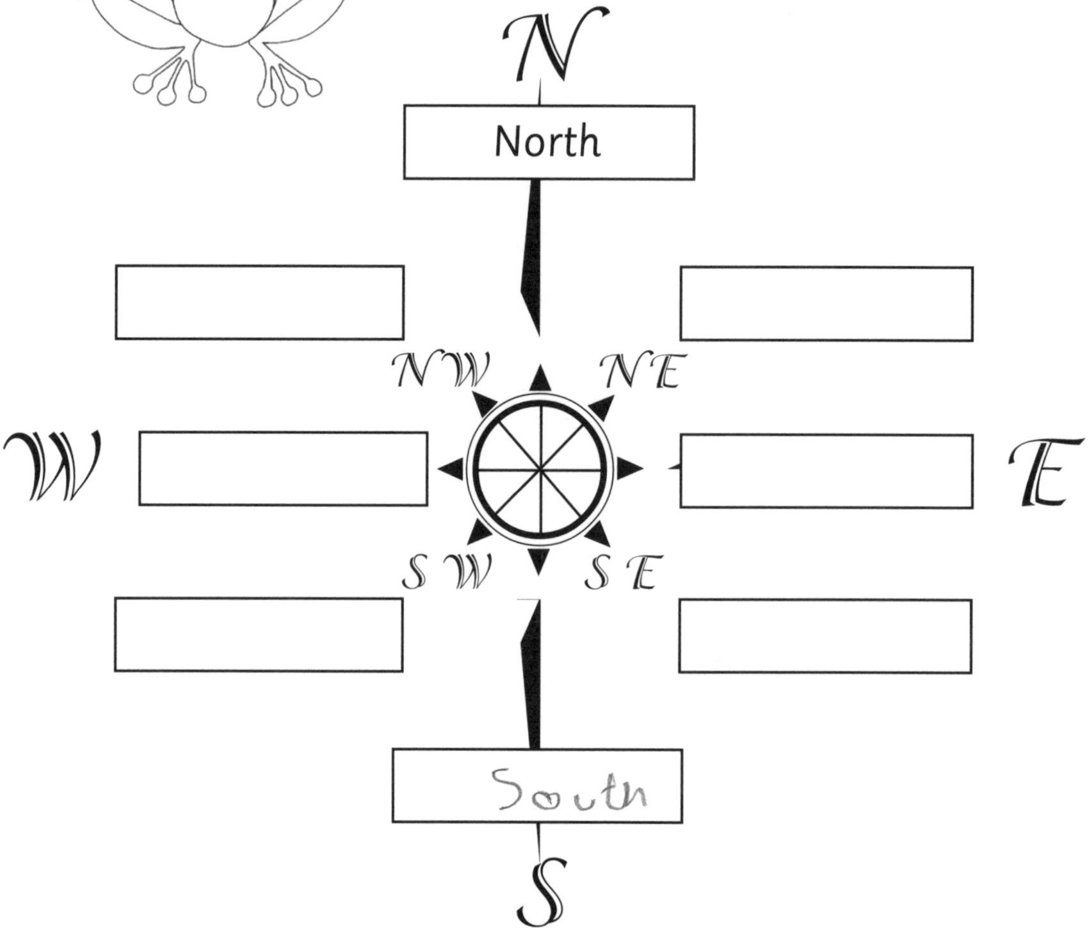

N

| North |

$N W$ $N E$

W E

$S W$ $S E$

| South |

S

Which compass direction is opposite to North?

Which compass direction is opposite to East?

Which compass direction is opposite to North-East?

Which compass direction is opposite to South-East?

Name: Date:

The Compass

Write the correct words in the boxes.
We have written North for you.

WORD BANK

North   South-West   East   North-East

South   North-West   South-East   West

$\mathcal{N}$

| North |

| North-West | | North-East |

$\mathcal{W}$ | West | | East | $\mathcal{E}$

| South-West | | South-East |

| South |

$\mathcal{S}$

Which compass direction is opposite to North? | South |

Which compass direction is opposite to East? | West |

Which compass direction is opposite to North-East? | South-West |

Which compass direction is opposite to South-East? | North-West |

Following Directions

Follow the instructions carefully.
Which square do you finish on?

Instructions:

1. Colour square D3
2. Move two squares North and colour the square.
3. Move four squares East and colour the square.
4. Move five squares North and colour the square.
5. Move five squares West and colour the square.
6. Move seven squares South and colour the square.

Which square have you finished on?

Now make up some instructions of your own and ask someone else to follow them.

Name: Date:

Following Directions

Follow the instructions carefully.
Which square do you finish on?

Instructions:

1. Colour square D3
2. Move two squares North and colour the square.
3. Move four squares East and colour the square.
4. Move five squares North and colour the square.
5. Move five squares West and colour the square.
6. Move seven squares South and colour the square.

Which square have you finished on?   C3

Now make up some instructions of your own and ask someone else to follow them.

Pond Survey

= 2 frogs

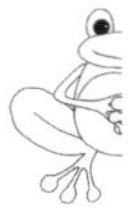

= 1 frog

I made a survey of my friends who live in four ponds.

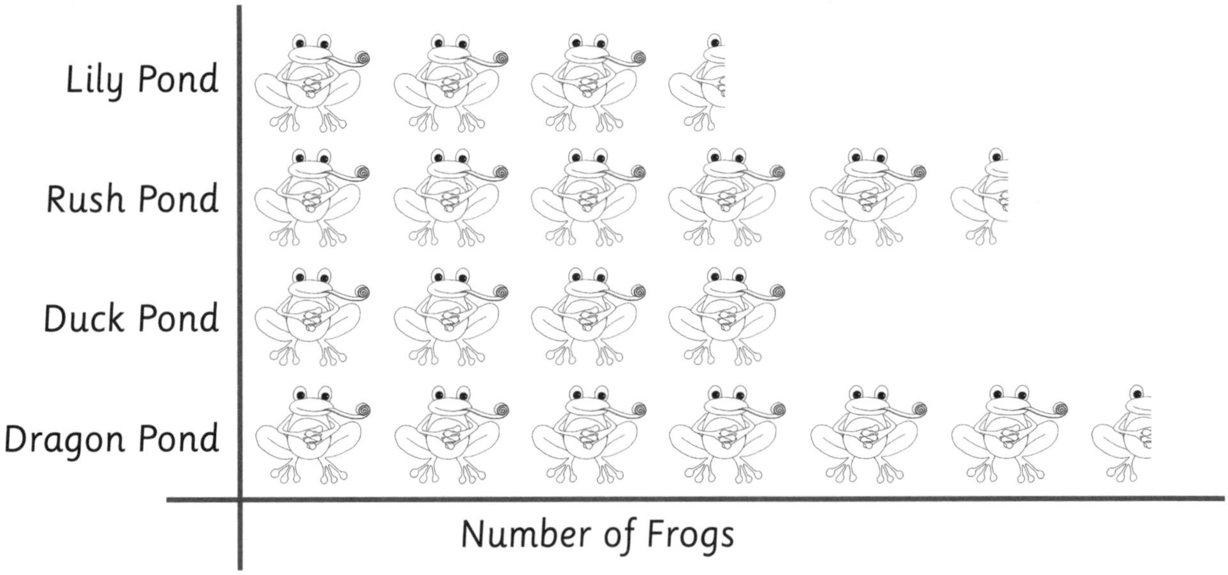

	Number of Frogs
Lily Pond	
Rush Pond	
Duck Pond	
Dragon Pond	

Number of Frogs

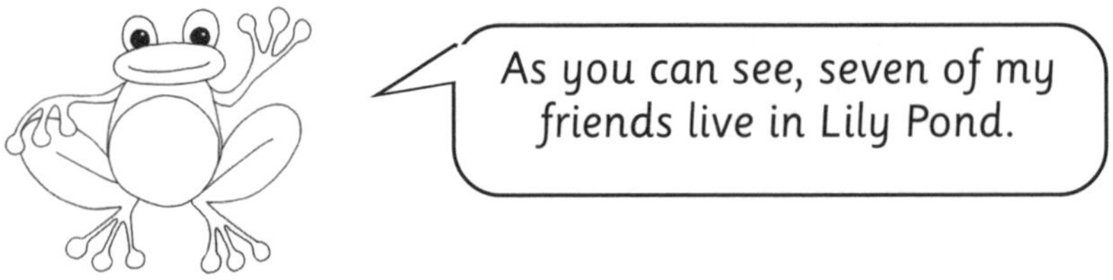

As you can see, seven of my friends live in Lily Pond.

1. How many of Frog's friends live in Rush Pond?

2. How many of Frog's friends live in Duck Pond?

3. How many of Frog's friends live in Dragon Pond?

4. How many frogs live in the four ponds altogether?

5. Which pond has most frogs?

6. Which pond has fewest frogs?

7. How many more frogs live in Duck Pond than Lily Pond?

8. How many fewer frogs live in Duck Pond than Dragon Pond?

Name: Date:

Pond Survey

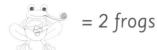 = 2 frogs

= 1 frog

I made a survey of my friends who live in four ponds.

Lily Pond

Rush Pond

Duck Pond

Dragon Pond

Number of Frogs

As you can see, seven of my friends live in Lily Pond.

1.	How many of Frog's friends live in Rush Pond?	11
2.	How many of Frog's friends live in Duck Pond?	8
3.	How many of Frog's friends live in Dragon Pond?	13
4.	How many frogs live in the four ponds altogether?	39
5.	Which pond has most frogs?	Dragon Pond
6.	Which pond has fewest frogs?	Lily Pond
7.	How many more frogs live in Duck Pond than Lily Pond?	1
8.	How many fewer frogs live in Duck Pond than Dragon Pond?	5

Adjectives

Adjectives (describing words) are used to describe nouns (naming words).

Underline the adjectives in the sentences below.

1. The sleek, black cat walked through the quiet street.
2. I enjoyed eating the crisp, crunchy carrot.
3. Please may I have some new, red shoes?
4. Around the rugged rock the ragged rascal ran.
5. The large, brown bear chased the terrified children.
6. I read an exciting book about green and blue monsters.

Now see if you can think of some adjectives to describe these nouns. (The first one is done for you.)

large   fierce

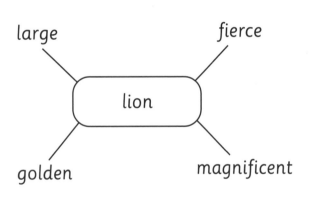
lion

golden   magnificent

cheese

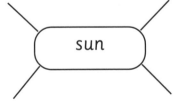
sun

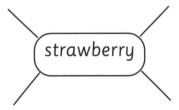
strawberry

Adjectives

Adjectives (describing words) are used to describe nouns (naming words).

> Underline the adjectives in the sentences below.

1. The <u>sleek</u>, <u>black</u> cat walked through the <u>quiet</u> street.
2. I enjoyed eating the <u>crisp, crunchy</u> carrot.
3. Please may I have some <u>new, red</u> shoes?
4. Around the <u>rugged</u> rock the <u>ragged</u> rascal ran.
5. The <u>large, brown</u> bear chased the <u>terrified</u> children.
6. I read an <u>exciting</u> book about <u>green</u> and <u>blue</u> monsters.

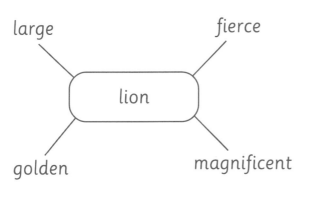

large   fierce

lion

golden   magnificent

> Now see if you can think of some adjectives to describe these nouns. (The first one is done for you.)

smelly   yellow

cheese

creamy   tasty

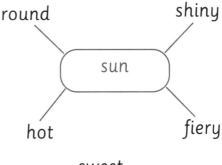

round   shiny

sun

hot   fiery

soft   sweet

strawberry

juicy   red

These are possible answers, though there are many more possibilities.

© Andrew Brodie *Publications* ✓ www.acblack.com

Number 19

Homework Today

Name: Date:

Verbs

Verbs are doing words. Think of a verb for each letter of the alphabet. There are lots to choose from.

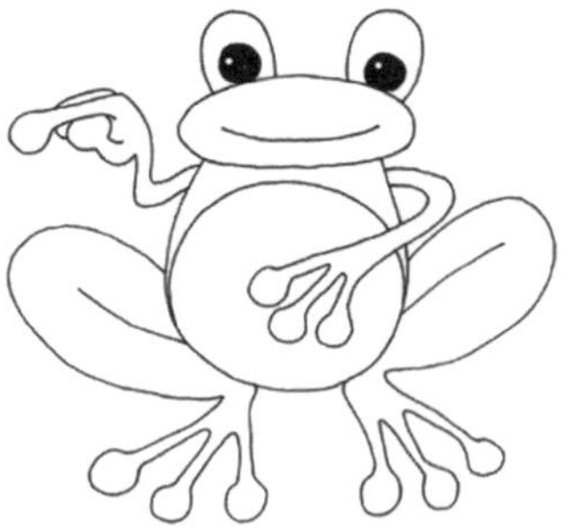

A

B

C

D

E

F

G

H

I

J

K

L

M

N

O

P

Q

R

S

T

U

V

W

X

Y

Z

Check your verbs by putting 'I can' in front of them.

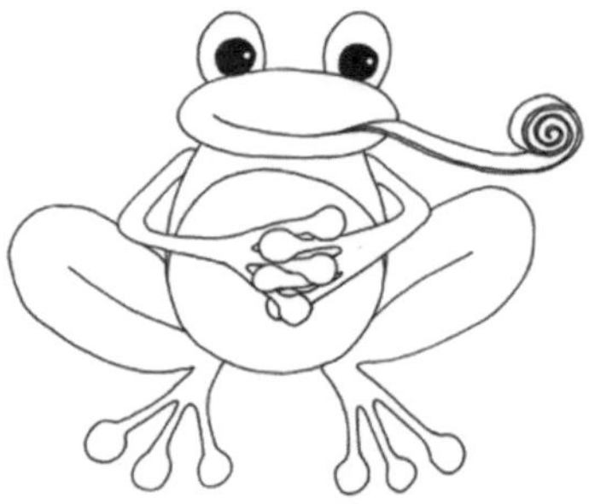

Name: Date:

Verbs

Verbs are doing words. Think of a verb for each letter of the alphabet. There are lots to choose from.

These are possible words to include.
There are many others you could use.

A	argue / ask
B	break / beat
C	climb / cry
D	dig / dream
E	enter / escape
F	feel / fall
G	go / grab / get
H	hop / help / hope
I	interfere / ignore
J	jog / jump
K	keep / kiss / kneel
L	leap / lift
M	munch / make
N	nip / nibble
O	operate / offer
P	peel / pour / pick

Q	quarrel / quit / quiver
R	run / read
S	see / sing
T	try / trip
U	undo / understand
V	visit / vibrate
W	write / weigh
X	x-ray
Y	yell / yawn
Z	zoom

Check your verbs by putting 'I can' in front of them.

Homework Today

Name: Date:

More Verbs

Using interesting verbs (doing words) helps to make your writing more exciting.

Choose two or three verbs that have a similar meaning to each of the verbs below. The first two have been done for you.

eat   →   gobble   munch   chew

look   →   stare   ogle   gaze

laugh   →   _____

run   →   _____

walk   →   _____

turn   →   _____

hurry   →   _____

Now put a verb into each of the following sentences to complete them.

1. I can _____ a book.

2. I enjoyed _____ that apple.

3. Oh dear, I _____ the glass.

4. Joseph _____ with his toys.

5. He _____ a high mountain.

6. Last week she _____ six lengths of the pool.

Name: Date:

More Verbs

Using interesting verbs (doing words) helps to make your writing more exciting.

Choose two or three verbs that have a similar meaning to each of the verbs below. The first two have been done for you.

eat	→	gobble	munch	chew
look	→	stare	ogle	gaze
laugh	→	chuckle	snigger	giggle
run	→	jog	trot	sprint
walk	→	stroll	amble	saunter
turn	→	spin	rotate	revolve
hurry	→	rush	speed	hasten

These are a few of the possible verbs.

Now put a verb into each of the following sentences to complete them.

1. I can __read__ a book.

2. I enjoyed __eating__ that apple.

3. Oh dear, I __smashed__ the glass.

4. Joseph __played__ with his toys.

5. He __climbed__ a high mountain.

6. Last week she __swam__ six lengths of the pool.

These are some of the possible answers.

Name: Date:

Spelling

Complete the answers by using: ee, ea or ie.
You may need to use a dictionary.

1. A loud yell.

s	c	r			m

2. A woolly animal.

s	h		p

3. Protection used by knights.

s	h		l	d

4. Walk quietly.

c	r		p

5. Do this in bed.

s	l		p

6. Cows may live here.

f		l	d

7. Selfish or spiteful.

m		n

8. Beef and pork are types of:

m		t

9. When people get together.

m		t

10. An extreme slope.

s	t		p

Did you notice that all the missing letters make an 'ee' sound?

Think of some more 'ee' sounding words and write them in the space below. I have started it for you.

yield   dream   extreme   feet

_____   _____   _____   _____

_____   _____   _____

Name: Date:

Spelling

Complete the answers by using: ee, ea or ie.
You may need to use a dictionary.

1. A loud yell.

| s | c | r | e | a | m |

2. A woolly animal.

| s | h | e | e | p |

3. Protection used by knights.

| s | h | i | e | l | d |

4. Walk quietly.

| c | r | e | e | p |

5. Do this in bed.

| s | l | e | e | p |

6. Cows may live here.

| f | i | e | l | d |

7. Selfish or spiteful.

| m | e | a | n |

8. Beef and pork are types of:

| m | e | a | t |

9. When people get together.

| m | e | e | t |

10. An extreme slope.

| s | t | e | e | p |

Did you notice that all
the missing letters make
an 'ee' sound?

Think of some more 'ee' sounding
words and write them in the space
below. I have started it for you.

The following are possibilities. There are many other correct answers.

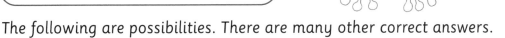

yield   dream   extreme   feet

feel   speed   steal   treat   meal

machine   steam   team

Name: _____ Date: _____

Technical Vocabulary

Read the words below. Do you
know what each word means?

alphabet	fiction	synonym	prefix
rhyme	illustration	verb	title
vowel	consonant	syllable	antonym
noun	suffix	singular	plural
punctuation	glossary	adjective	apostrophe

Now find all the words in the
word search below.

a	l	p	h	a	b	e	t	a	b	d	e	g	s	l	p	u	n	c	t	u	a	t	i	o	n
p	m	r	a	t	t	h	i	w	e	n	c	j	y	o	a	l	s	o	o	e	e	l	l	e	o
o	p	e	s	z	w	n	t	o	n	y	f	i	l	i	s	i	n	g	u	l	a	r	l	e	u
s	e	f	n	a	g	l	l	i	s	h	m	a	l	y	s	f	i	e	l	d	n	r	a	b	n
t	t	i	o	n	w	v	e	r	b	n	f	l	a	e	g	g	b	s	u	r	p	g	h	n	o
r	r	x	f	t	o	l	k	s	n	t	r	o	b	h	i	n	o	y	i	n	l	g	l	f	y
o	e	x	n	o	r	j	v	o	w	e	l	t	l	a	e	i	o	n	u	s	u	f	f	i	x
p	g	r	a	n	j	u	h	a	m	d	i	t	e	h	b	b	a	o	r	b	r	a	r	c	x
h	o	b	o	y	s	l	s	t	r	u	z	y	x	m	o	h	o	n	v	i	a	n	g	t	t
e	u	s	e	m	t	t	c	o	n	s	o	n	a	n	t	e	e	y	a	b	l	c	d	i	r
e	f	g	h	o	p	q	l	l	g	r	d	i	s	i	s	i	s	m	b	r	e	d	t	o	e
i	r	h	y	m	e	r	s	t	e	e	i	k	l	q	u	s	n	l	a	s	t	u	w	n	e
j	m	y	o	i	n	b	a	d	j	e	c	t	i	v	e	l	m	a	u	y	e	t	v	r	z
k	n	e	w	g	o	u	v	w	n	t	h	w	n	s	t	i	s	a	r	t	l	m	o	t	e
l	i	l	l	u	s	t	r	a	t	i	o	n	s	s	l	r	x	g	l	o	s	s	a	r	y

Name: Date:

Technical Vocabulary

Read the words below. Do you
know what each word means?

alphabet	synonym	prefix
rhyme	verb	title
vowel	syllable	antonym
noun	singular	plural
punctuation	adjective	apostrophe

Now find all the words in the
word search below.

a	l	p	h	a	b	e	t	a	b	d	e	g	s	l	p	u	n	c	t	u	a	t	i	o	n
p	m	r	a	t	t	h	i	w	e	n	c	j	y	o	a	l	s	o	o	e	e	l	l	e	o
o	p	e	s	z	w	n	t	o	n	y	f	i	l	i	s	i	n	g	u	l	a	r	l	e	u
s	e	f	n	a	g	l	l	i	s	h	m	a	l	y	s	f	i	e	l	d	n	r	a	b	n
t	t	i	o	n	w	v	e	r	b	n	f	l	a	e	g	g	b	s	u	r	p	g	h	n	o
r	r	x	f	t	o	l	k	s	n	t	r	o	b	h	i	n	o	y	i	n	l	g	l	f	y
o	e	x	n	o	r	j	v	o	w	e	l	t	l	a	e	i	o	n	u	s	u	f	f	i	x
p	g	r	a	n	j	u	h	a	m	d	i	t	e	h	b	b	a	o	r	b	r	a	r	c	x
h	o	b	o	y	s	l	s	t	r	u	z	y	x	m	o	h	o	n	v	i	a	n	g	t	t
e	u	s	e	m	t	t	c	o	n	s	o	n	a	n	t	e	e	y	a	b	l	c	d	i	r
e	f	g	h	o	p	q	l	l	g	r	d	i	s	i	s	i	s	m	b	r	e	d	t	o	e
i	r	h	y	m	e	r	s	t	e	e	i	k	l	q	u	s	n	l	a	s	t	u	w	n	e
j	m	y	o	i	n	b	a	d	j	e	c	t	i	v	e	l	m	a	u	y	e	t	v	r	z
k	n	e	w	g	o	u	v	w	n	t	h	w	n	s	t	i	s	a	r	t	l	m	o	t	e
l	i	l	l	u	s	t	r	a	t	i	o	n	s	s	l	r	x	g	l	o	s	s	a	r	y

Synonyms

A synonym is a word that means the same (or very nearly the same) as another word.

Write a synonym for each of the following words. The first one has been done for you.

bucket → pail   moan → _____

prison → _____   smile → _____

shovel → _____   floor → _____

battle → _____   laugh → _____

jump → _____   silent → _____

fast → _____   big → _____

Now use your synonyms to replace the words in brackets in the following sentences.

1. She dropped her toys on the (floor) _____.

2. She took a bucket and (shovel) _____ to the beach.

3. The room was (silent) _____ when the children were all working hard.

4. The joke made them all (laugh) _____ .

5. It was a very (big)_____ birthday cake.

Name: Date:

Synonyms

A synonym is a word that means the same (or very nearly the same) as another word.

Write a synonym for each of the following words. The first one has been done for you.

bucket	→	pail	moan →	groan
prison	→	jail or gaol	smile →	grin
shovel	→	spade	floor →	ground
battle	→	fight	laugh →	chuckle
jump	→	leap	silent →	quiet
fast	→	speedy	big →	large

The answers given are those most likely to be chosen. There are other, equally good, possibilities.

Now use your synonyms to replace the words in brackets in the following sentences.

1. She dropped her toys on the (floor) _____ground_____ .

2. She took a bucket and (shovel) _____spade_____ to the beach.

3. The room was (silent) _____quiet_____ when the children were all working hard.

4. The joke made them all (laugh) _____chuckle_____ .

5. It was a very (big) _____large_____ birthday cake.

Number

24

Homework Today

Name: Date:

Antonyms and Compound Words

Antonyms are words that mean the opposite of each other.

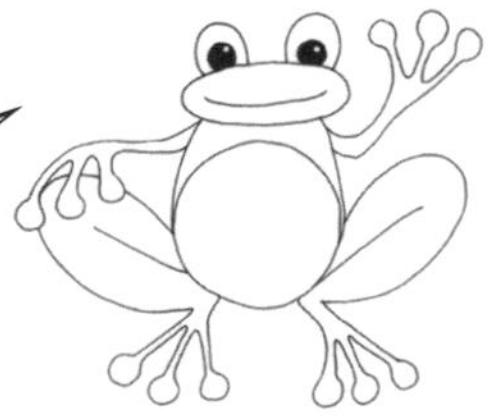

Choose words from the word bank to complete the pairs of antonyms.

less down last sad enemy light
after out under slow

up ➔		more ➔	
over ➔		friend ➔	
dark ➔		first ➔	
before ➔		fast ➔	
in ➔		happy ➔	

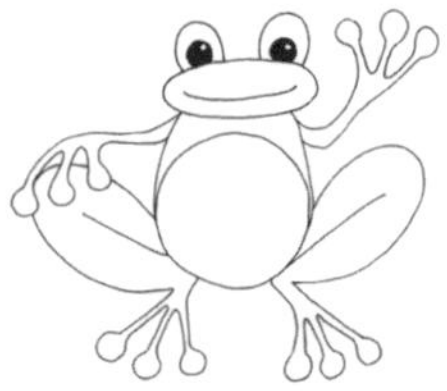

Compound words are words made from two or more shorter words.

Turn these twenty-four words into twelve new compound words.

light pot play cup up shoe out air pad
stairs place rain fire bow day port side
lock ship board lace friend tea ground

Name: Date:

Antonyms and Compound Words

Antonyms are words that mean
the opposite of each other.

Choose words from the word bank to complete the pairs of antonyms.

> less   down   last   sad   enemy   light
> after   out   under   slow

up → | down
over → | under
dark → | light
before → | after
in → | out

more → | less
friend → | enemy
first → | last
fast → | slow
happy → | sad

Compound words are words made
from two or more shorter words.

Turn these twenty-four words into twelve new compound words.

> light   pot   play   cup   up   shoe   out   air   pad
> stairs   place   rain   fire   bow   day   port   side
> lock   ship   board   lace   friend   tea   ground

shoelace	playground	padlock
airport	upstairs	outside
teapot	friendship	fireplace
cupboard	daylight	rainbow

Other possible answers include: teacup, airship and outboard.

Silent Letters

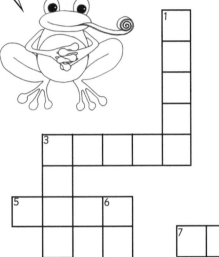

Follow the clues to complete my 'words with silent letters' puzzle.

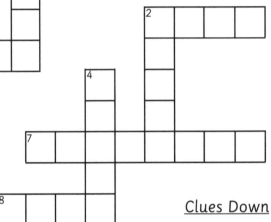

words to help you:

write   knock   lamb   comb
bomb   knee   gnome   climb
wrinkled   gnat

Clues Down

1. Communicate on paper.
2. Bump.
3. Small biting insect.
4. Go up a mountain.
6. Explosive device.

Clues Across

2. Leg joint
3. Small stone person,
   sometimes seen in gardens.
5. Young sheep.
7. Creased or crumpled.
8. Use this in your hair.

Make a list of other words that begin or end with a silent letter.

Name: Date:

Silent Letters

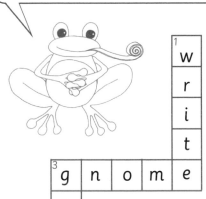

Follow the clues to complete my 'words with silent letters' puzzle.

words to help you:

write   knock   lamb   comb
bomb   knee   gnome   climb
wrinkled   gnat

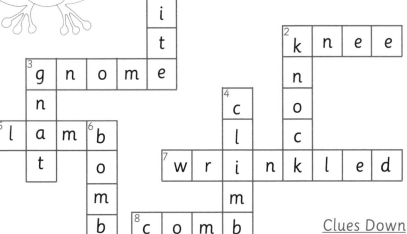

Clues Across

2.   Leg joint
3.   Small stone person, sometimes seen in gardens.
5.   Young sheep.
7.   Creased or crumpled.
8.   Use this in your hair.

Clues Down

1.   Communicate on paper.
2.   Bump.
3.   Small biting insect.
4.   Go up a mountain.
6.   Explosive device.

These are just some possible answers.

know	wrong
limb	honour
wrist	knot
honest	knife
kneel	wrap
crumb	thumb

Make a list of other words that begin or end with a silent letter.

Contractions

Help me to shorten my sentences by making two words into one.

Use the ideas below to help you.

could not	→	couldn't
should not	→	shouldn't
can not	→	can't
are not	→	aren't
we are	→	we're

do not	→	don't
shall not	→	shan't
have not	→	haven't
they are	→	they're

Remember to put in the apostrophe!

1.   I can not remember my eight times table.

_____

2.   He should not go out alone.

_____

3.   I have not got enough money.

_____

4.   They are all eight years old.

_____

5.   In the summer we are going on holiday.

_____

Can you think of some more shortened words and write them on the back of this sheet ?

Name: Date:

Contractions

Help me to shorten my sentences by making two words into one.

Use the ideas below to help you.

could not	→	couldn't
should not	→	shouldn't
can not	→	can't
are not	→	aren't
we are	→	we're

do not	→	don't
shall not	→	shan't
have not	→	haven't
they are	→	they're

Remember to put in the apostrophe!

1. I can not remember my eight times table.

    I can't remember my eight times table.

2. He should not go out alone.

    He shouldn't go out alone.

3. I have not got enough money.

    I haven't got enough money.

4. They are all eight years old.

    They're all eight years old.

5. In the summer we are going on holiday.

    In the summer we're going on holiday.

Can you think of some more shortened words and write them on the back of this sheet ?

Name: Date:

Common Prefixes

A prefix is put in front of a word to make a new word.

Find the opposite to each of these words by
using the prefixes: un, il, im or dis.

happy	→	
legal	→	
comfortable	→	
appear	→	
trust	→	
mobile	→	
practical	→	
able	→	
possible	→	

Now make new words from the words
below by adding the prefixes: re, pre or de.

			c	a	u	t	i	o	n

		d	o

		p	r	e	s	s

			v	i	e	w

			t	e	n	d

			r	a	i	l

		c	o	v	e	r

			s	e	n	t

			c	a	l	l

		l	i	g	h	t

			t	u	r	n

Name: Date:

Common Prefixes

A prefix is put in front of a word to make a new word.

Find the opposite to each of these words by
using the prefixes: un, il, im or dis.

happy	→	unhappy
legal	→	illegal
comfortable	→	uncomfortable
appear	→	disappear
trust	→	distrust
mobile	→	immobile
practical	→	impractical
able	→	unable or disable
possible	→	impossible

Now make new words from the words
below by adding the prefixes: re, pre or de.

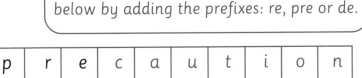

p	r	e	c	a	u	t	i	o	n

r	e	d	o

d	e	p	r	e	s	s

p	r	e	t	e	n	d

r	e	v	i	e	w

r	e	c	o	v	e	r

d	e	r	a	i	l

p	r	e	s	e	n	t

r	e	c	a	l	l

d	e	l	i	g	h	t

r	e	t	u	r	n

Name: Date:

Comprehension

It was a bright sunny April morning, and Little Red Riding Hood was looking forward to her walk to Grandma's house. She was ten years old and it was the very first time she had been allowed to walk along the woodland paths on her own. Mother gave her a basket to carry, and in it was a freshly cooked apple pie; Grandma's favourite.

Answer the questions using a good sentence for each answer. I have done the first one for you.

1.   How old was Little Red Riding Hood?

_____Little Red Riding Hood was ten years old._____

2.   What was the weather like that morning?

_____

3.   What flavour pie did Grandma like best?

_____

4.   Had Little Red Riding Hood been to Grandma's house alone before?

_____

5.   At what time of year did the story take place?

_____

6.   Where did Mother put the apple pie?

_____

Name: Date:

Comprehension

It was a bright sunny April morning, and Little Red Riding Hood was looking forward to her walk to Grandma's house. She was ten years old and it was the very first time she had been allowed to walk along the woodland paths on her own. Mother gave her a basket to carry, and in it was a freshly cooked apple pie; Grandma's favourite.

Answer the questions using a good sentence for each answer. I have done the first one for you.

1. How old was Little Red Riding Hood?

   Little Red Riding Hood was ten years old.

2. What was the weather like that morning?

   It was a bright sunny morning.

3. What flavour pie did Grandma like best?

   Grandma liked apple pie best.

4. Had Little Red Riding Hood been to Grandma's house alone before?

   No, Little Red Riding Hood had not been to Grandma's house alone.

5. At what time of year did the story take place?

   The story took place in April (or in spring).

6. Where did Mother put the apple pie?

   Mother put the apple pie into a basket.

These are sample answers. There are other equally correct variations.

Capital Letters

Capital letters are used at the beginning of sentences, new lines of a poem, titles, names of people, places, months, days and for the word I.

Rewrite the following items, inserting the missing capital letters.

1. last year i visited england, scotland, ireland and wales.

_____

2. my sister celia and my brother richard went out with me.

_____

3. old mother hubbard,

_____

she went to the cupboard

_____

to get the poor dog a bone;

_____

but when she got there

_____

the cupboard was bare

_____

and so the poor dog had none.

_____

4. i saw elephants, zebras and kangaroos at the zoo.

_____

5. my birthday is on monday the sixth of august.

_____

Name: Date:

Capital Letters

Capital letters are used at the beginning of sentences, new lines of a poem, titles, names of people, places, months, days and for the word I.

Rewrite the following items, inserting the missing capital letters.

1.   last year i visited england, scotland, ireland and wales.

   Last year I visited England, Scotland, Ireland and Wales.

2.   my sister celia and my brother richard went out with me.

   My sister Celia and my brother Richard went out with me.

3.   old mother hubbard,

   Old mother Hubbard,

   she went to the cupboard

   She went to the cupboard

   to get the poor dog a bone;

   To get the poor dog a bone;

   but when she got there

   But when she got there

   the cupboard was bare

   The cupboard was bare

   and so the poor dog had none.

   And so the poor dog had none.

4.   i saw elephants, zebras and kangaroos at the zoo.

   I saw elephants, zebras and kangaroos at the zoo.

5.   my birthday is on monday the sixth of august.

   My birthday is on Monday the sixth of August.

Commas

When you put commas in a list you do not need to put one before the word 'and'.

Put commas in these sentences to separate the items in each list.

1. January March May July August October and December each have thirty-one days.

2. In the shop I bought cheese eggs milk butter and potatoes.

3. There were elephants tigers giraffes koalas zebras lions and many other animals at the zoo.

4. To make this model you will need card glue scissors a ruler and some coloured pencils.

5. Red orange yellow green blue indigo and violet are the colours of the rainbow.

6. Please put knives forks spoons plates and glasses on the table.

Look to see if you have put in all the twenty-four commas where necessary.

Now write three sentences of your own, on the back of this sheet. Include a list in each sentence.

Commas

> When you put commas in a list you do not need to put one before the word 'and'.

Put commas in these sentences to separate the items in each list.

1. January, March, May, July, August, October and December each have thirty-one days.

2. In the shop I bought cheese, eggs, milk, butter and potatoes.

3. There were elephants, tigers, giraffes, koalas, zebras, lions and many other animals at the zoo.

4. To make this model you will need card, glue, scissors, a ruler and some coloured pencils.

5. Red, orange, yellow, green, blue, indigo and violet are the colours of the rainbow.

6. Please put knives, forks, spoons, plates and glasses on the table.

> Look to see if you have put in all the twenty-four commas where necessary.

Now write three sentences of your own, on the back of this sheet. Include a list in each sentence.

Name: Date:

Speech Marks

Rewrite the sentences adding speech marks and choosing more interesting words than 'said'. I have done the first one for you.

Words to help you:

whispered   demanded   requested
yelled   groaned   laughed

1. Please may I have more cake <u>said</u> Graham.

<u>"Please may I have more cake?" requested Graham.</u>

2. That was very funny, <u>said</u> mum.

_____

3. The zoo keeper <u>said</u>, be very quiet near these animals.

_____

4. It's a goal, <u>said</u> the players.

_____

5. I feel very ill, <u>said</u> the boy.

_____

6. Give me more sweets <u>said</u> the girl.

_____

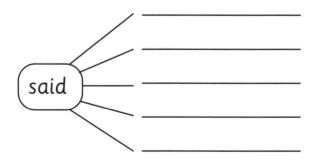

said

Now try to think of five more words you can use instead of 'said'.

Speech Marks

Rewrite the sentences adding speech marks and choosing more interesting words than 'said'. I have done the first one for you.

Words to help you:

whispered   demanded   requested

yelled   groaned   laughed

1.   Please may I have more cake <u>said</u> Graham.

<u>"Please may I have more cake?" requested Graham.</u>

2.   That was very funny, <u>said</u> mum.

<u>"That was very funny," laughed mum.</u>

3.   The zoo keeper <u>said</u>, be very quiet near these animals.

<u>The zoo keeper whispered, "Be very quiet near these animals."</u>

4.   It's a goal, <u>said</u> the players.

<u>"It's a goal!" yelled the players.</u>

5.   I feel very ill, <u>said</u> the boy.

<u>"I feel very ill," groaned the boy.</u>

6.   Give me more sweets <u>said</u> the girl.

<u>"Give me more sweets," demanded the girl.</u>

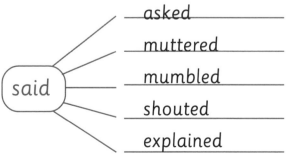

said
— asked
— muttered
— mumbled
— shouted
— explained

Now try to think of five more words you can use instead of 'said'.

These are just a few examples of possible answers; there are many equally acceptable ones.

Punctuation

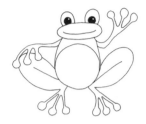

Please rewrite the sentences for me, and insert the correct punctuation.

dont do that yelled the boys

_____

why do pigs have curly tails

_____

october is the month after september said the teacher

_____

_____

you can buy cheese bacon cucumber tomatoes and bananas from the shop

_____

_____

is that a new car fred asked his friend

_____

oh no exclaimed mum

_____

Did you find all the speech marks, question marks, exclamation marks, commas, capital letters and full stops?

Name: Date:

Punctuation

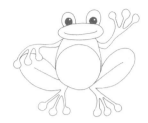

Please rewrite the sentences for me, and insert the correct punctuation.

dont do that yelled the boys

"Don't do that!" yelled the boys.

why do pigs have curly tails

Why do pigs have curly tails?

october is the month after september said the teacher

"October is the month after September," said the teacher.

you can buy cheese bacon cucumber tomatoes and bananas from the shop

You can buy cheese, bacon, cucumber, tomatoes

and bananas from the shop.

is that a new car fred asked his friend

"Is that a new car?" Fred asked his friend.

OR   "Is that a new car, Fred?" asked his friend.

oh no exclaimed Mum

"Oh no!" exclaimed Mum.

Did you find all the speech marks, question marks, exclamation marks, commas, capital letters and full stops?

World Religions

Read this with care.

There are several main world religions; these include Buddhism, Christianity, Hinduism, Islam, Judaism and Sikhism. There are also many other less well known faiths.

Each religion has a special building where people gather together to worship. Christians worship in churches, Buddhists and Hindus worship in temples, Jews worship in synagogues, Muslims worship in mosques and Sikhs worship in gurdwaras. People may also worship in their own homes. All of the main religions value caring about others, honesty and leading a good life.

Now use the information to complete the page.

Name six major world religions.

Draw a line to match the name of the building to the people who worship there:

Christians   Temple

Jews (Judaism)   Mosque

Muslims (Islam)   Synagogue

Sikhs   Church

Hindus   Gurdwara

Buddhists

Name: Date:

World Religions

Read this with care.

There are several main world religions; these include Buddhism, Christianity, Hinduism, Islam, Judaism and Sikhism. There are also many other less well known faiths.

Each religion has a special building where people gather together to worship. Christians worship in churches, Buddhists and Hindus worship in temples, Jews worship in synagogues, Muslims worship in mosques and Sikhs worship in gurdwaras. People may also worship in their own homes. All of the main religions value caring about others, honesty and leading a good life.

Now use the information to complete the page.

Name six major world religions.

Buddhism	Sikhism
Judaism	Hinduism
Christianity	Islam

Draw a line to match the name of the building
to the people who worship there:

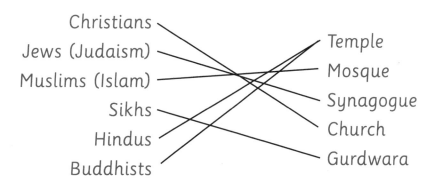

Christians — Temple
Jews (Judaism) — Mosque
Muslims (Islam) — Synagogue
Sikhs — Church
Hindus — Gurdwara
Buddhists

Hinduism

A glossary is a list of words, and their meanings. It is often found at the back of a book.

You might find this sort of glossary at the end of a book about Hinduism.

Brahma	→	One of the three main Hindu Gods. Brahma is the creator.
Diwali	→	A festival, usually held in October or November.
Holi	→	A Hindu festival held in the spring.
Shiva	→	One of the three main Hindu Gods. Shiva is the destroyer.
Temple	→	The building for Hindu worship.
Vishnu	→	One of the three main Hindu Gods. Vishnu is the preserver.

Now use the glossary to answer the questions.

1. Is the word list in a special order?

    What is this order called?

2. Name the three main Hindu Gods.

3. Name two Hindu festivals.

4. What is a Temple used for?

Name: Date:

Hinduism

A glossary is a list of words, and their meanings. It is often found at the back of a book.

You might find this sort of glossary at the end of a book about Hinduism.

Brahma   →   One of the three main Hindu Gods. Brahma is the creator.

Diwali   →   A festival, usually held in October or November.

Holi   →   A Hindu festival held in the spring.

Shiva   →   One of the three main Hindu Gods. Shiva is the destroyer.

Temple   →   The building for Hindu worship.

Vishnu   →   One of the three main Hindu Gods. Vishnu is the preserver.

Now use the glossary to answer the questions.

1.   Is the word list in a special order? | Yes |

    What is this order called? | Alphabetical order |

2.   Name the three main Hindu Gods.

| Brahma | Shiva | Vishnu |

3.   Name two Hindu festivals.

| Diwali | Holi |

4.   What is a Temple used for?

| A temple is a Hindu place of worship. |

Name: Date:

Christianity Crossword

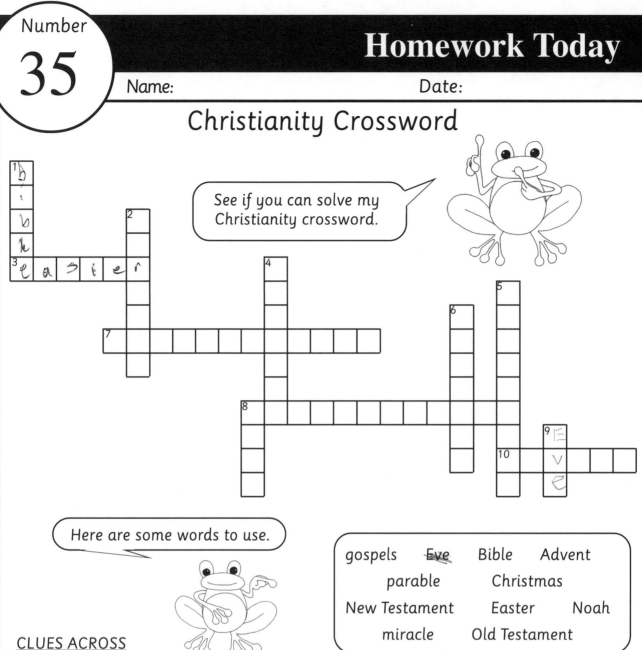

See if you can solve my Christianity crossword.

Here are some words to use.

gospels   ~~Eve~~   Bible   Advent
parable   Christmas
New Testament   Easter   Noah
miracle   Old Testament

CLUES ACROSS

3. Time when the crucifixion and resurrection are celebrated.
7. Part of Bible concerned with time before the birth of Jesus Christ.
8. Part of Bible dealing with the time after the birth of Jesus.
10. Time of preparing for Christmas.

CLUES DOWN

1. Book of religious writings.
2. Story, with a meaning told by Jesus Christ.
4. Impossible deeds performed by Jesus Christ.
5. Celebration of the birth of Christ.
6. The first four books of the New Testament (Matthew, Mark, Luke and John).
8. He built an ark.
9. First woman created by God, to be with Adam.

Christianity Crossword

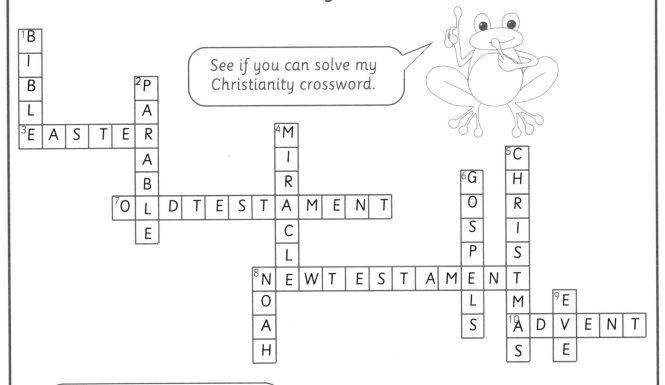

See if you can solve my Christianity crossword.

Here are some words to use.

gospels Eve Bible Advent
parable Christmas
New Testament Easter Noah
miracle Old Testament

CLUES ACROSS

3. Time when the crucifixion and resurrection are celebrated.
7. Part of Bible concerned with time before the birth of Jesus Christ.
8. Part of Bible dealing with the time after the birth of Jesus.
10. Time of preparing for Christmas.

CLUES DOWN

1. Book of religious writings.
2. Story, with a meaning told by Jesus Christ.
4. Impossible deeds performed by Jesus Christ.
5. Celebration of the birth of Christ.
6. The first four books of the New Testament (Matthew, Mark, Luke and John).
8. He built an ark.
9. First woman created by God, to be with Adam.

Name: Date:

Religious Celebrations

Here is a picture of a bride and groom at their Christian wedding celebration. This wedding took place in the year 1940, during the Second World War.

Look at the clothes.

Do you have any old photographs of religious celebrations in your house?

Look at the picture carefully and write about how you can tell that the picture is not a modern one.

_____

_____

_____

_____

_____

_____

_____

Religious Celebrations

Here is a picture of a bride and groom at their Christian wedding celebration. This wedding took place in the year 1940, during the Second World War.

Look at the clothes.

Do you have any old photographs of religious celebrations in your house?

Look at the picture carefully and write about how you can tell that the picture is not a modern one.

Answers could include such points as:

The style of the bride's dress is not modern, neither is her hair style.

The dress is not a traditional wedding dress due to clothes rationing.

The groom's beret is an older style, and he is being married in uniform.

Children will probably mention the photograph being black and white.

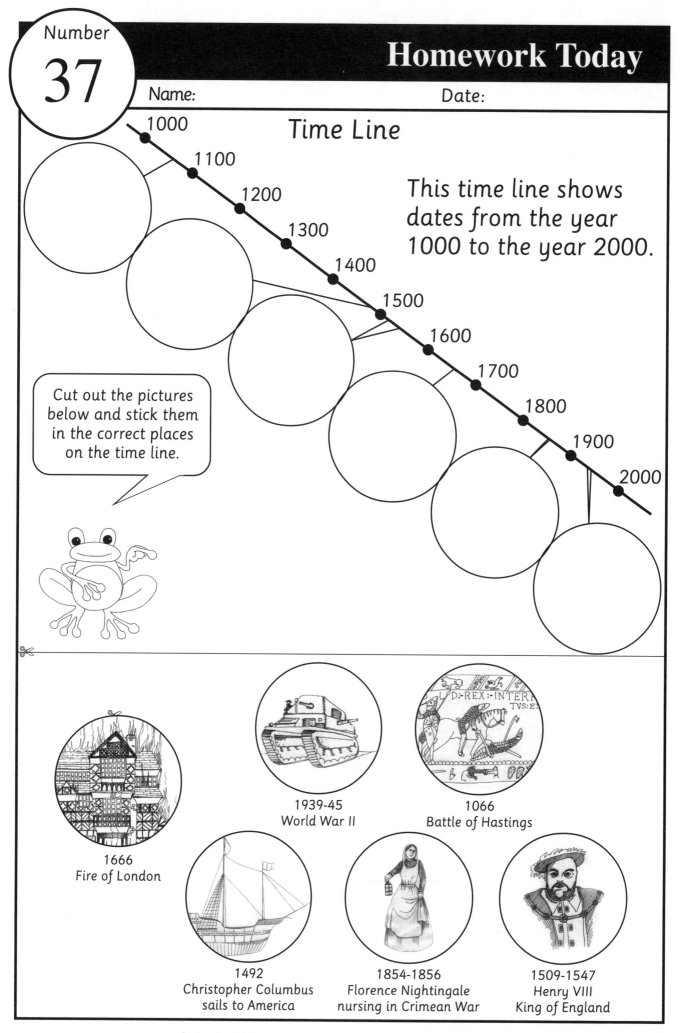

Time Line

This time line shows dates from the year 1000 to the year 2000.

1000
1100
1200
1300
1400
1500
1600
1700
1800
1900
2000

Cut out the pictures below and stick them in the correct places on the time line.

1666
Fire of London

1939-45
World War II

1066
Battle of Hastings

1492
Christopher Columbus
sails to America

1854-1856
Florence Nightingale
nursing in Crimean War

1509-1547
Henry VIII
King of England

© Andrew Brodie *Publications* ✓ www.acblack.com

Name: Date:

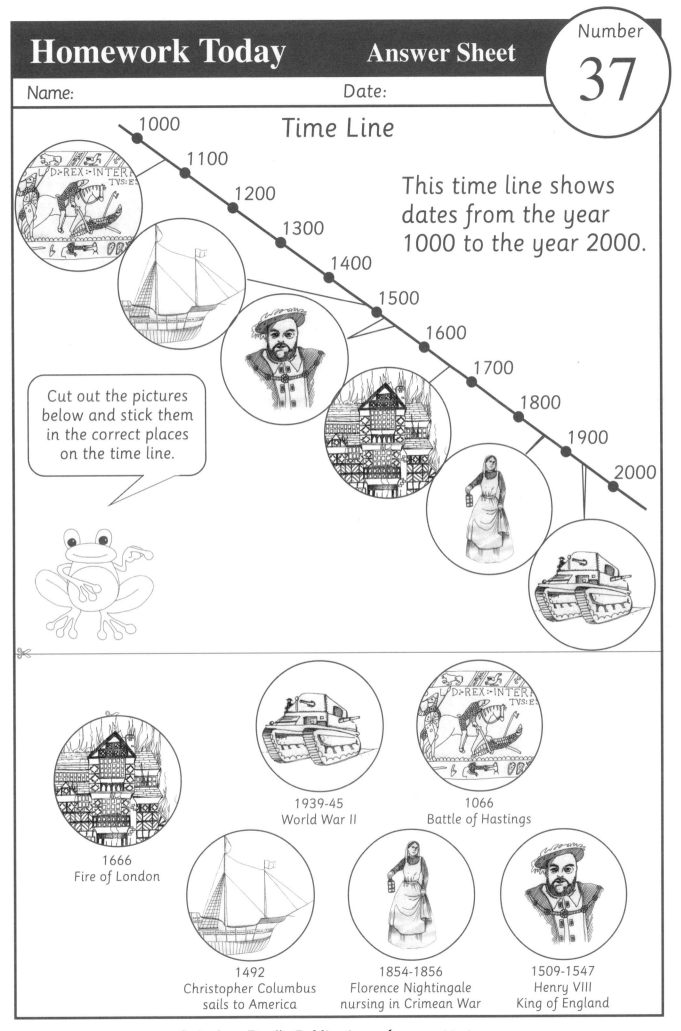

Time Line

This time line shows dates from the year 1000 to the year 2000.

1000
1100
1200
1300
1400
1500
1600
1700
1800
1900
2000

Cut out the pictures below and stick them in the correct places on the time line.

1939-45
World War II

1066
Battle of Hastings

1666
Fire of London

1492
Christopher Columbus
sails to America

1854-1856
Florence Nightingale
nursing in Crimean War

1509-1547
Henry VIII
King of England

© Andrew Brodie *Publications* ✓ www.acblack.com

Name: Date:

The Vikings

Use labels from the box for these
Viking pictures.

A word written in runes.
A Viking longship.
A circular shield.
Viking men and women wore brooches.
A double-edged sword.
A helmet with nose shield.

You may colour the pictures.
Think carefully about the best
colours to use.

Name: Date:

The Vikings

Use labels from the box for these Viking pictures.

> A word written in runes.
> A Viking longship.
> A circular shield.
> Viking men and women wore brooches.
> A double-edged sword.
> A helmet with nose shield.

A Viking longship.

A helmet with nose-shield.

A double-edged sword.

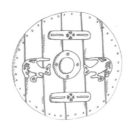

A circular shield.

A word written in runes.

Viking men and women wore brooches.

You may colour the pictures. Think carefully about the best colours to use.

Name: Date:

Musical Instruments

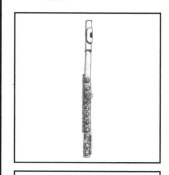

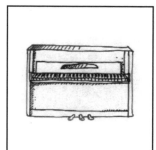

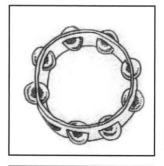

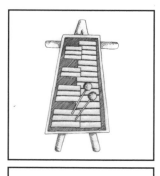

Label each picture correctly. Here are some words to help you.

tuba   trumpet   violin   triangle   xylophone   drums
flute   piano   recorder   guitar   tambourine

Use the last box to draw and label another musical instrument you know.

Name: Date:

Musical Instruments

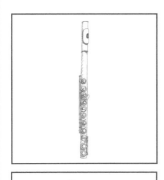

flute

guitar

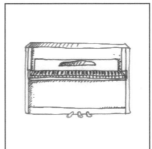

piano

recorder

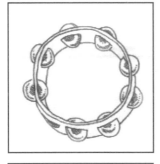

tambourine

triangle

trumpet

violin

xylophone

drums

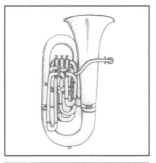

tuba

Label each picture correctly. Here are some words to help you.

> tuba   trumpet   violin   triangle   xylophone   drums
> flute   piano   recorder   guitar   tambourine

Use the last box to draw and label another musical instrument you know.

Name: _____ Date: _____

Musical Terms

Using the words in the box, solve the clues to fill in the bars on my xylophone.

drum	song	dynamics	chorus	oboe
staccato	rhythm	beat	notation	trombone
pitch	guitar	compose	banana	verse

1. A tune with words. (s---)

2. A steady rhythmic sound. (b---)

3. This is usually before the chorus. (v----)

4. How high or low a note sounds. (p----)

5. This may follow each verse. (c-----)

6. Patterns of beats. (r-----)

7. Make up a new piece of music. (c------)

8. Written music. (n-------)

9. How loud or soft the music is. (d-------)

10. Shortened, separated notes. (s-------)

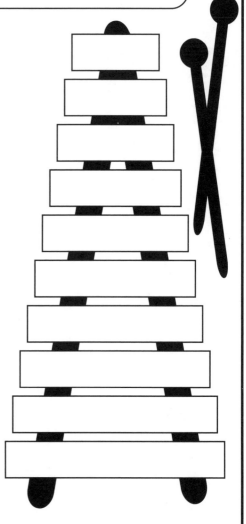

Write the remaining words from the box on the lines below.
Put a ring around the odd one out.

_____ _____ _____

_____ _____

Name: Date:

Musical Terms

Using the words in the box, solve the clues
to fill in the bars on my xylophone.

drum	song	dynamics	chorus	oboe
staccato	rhythm	beat	notation	trombone
pitch	guitar	compose	banana	verse

1. A tune with words.

2. A steady rhythmic sound.

3. This is usually before the chorus.

4. How high or low a note sounds.

5. This may follow each verse.

6. Patterns of beats.

7. Make up a new piece of music.

8. Written music.

9. How loud or soft the music is.

10. Shortened, separated notes.

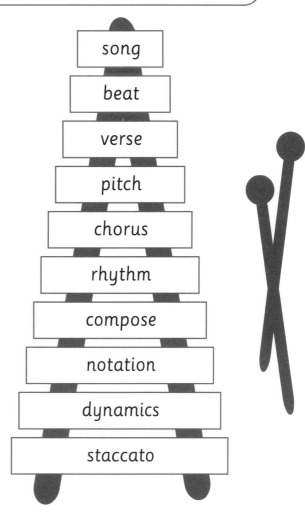

song
beat
verse
pitch
chorus
rhythm
compose
notation
dynamics
staccato

Write the remaining words from the box on the lines below.
Put a ring around the odd one out.

_____drum_____   _____guitar_____   (banana)

_____oboe_____   _____trombone_____

Name: _____ Date: _____

School

Answer these questions about school.

What do you like best about school?

_____Pe_____

Is there anything you dislike about school? If so, what is it?

_____same____things__we__baned_____

What are you good at?

_____Pe_____

What do you need more help with?

_____Maths_____

What do you hope to achieve at school this year?

_____handwriting_____

Now complete the list below. Write the name of your favourite subject at the top. By the time you get to the bottom you will be left with your least favourite subject.

_____Pe, history, art,_____

_____Literacy, information_____

_____technology, history,_____

_____science, geography, Re_____

_____numeracy, design_____

_____technology._____

_____

_____

_____

Subject Word Bank

Design Technology

~~Art~~ ~~PE~~ ~~RE~~ ~~Numeracy~~

~~Literacy~~ ~~Science~~

~~History~~ ~~Geography~~

~~Information Technology~~

Name: Date:

School

Answer these questions about school.

What do you like best about school?

The responses to these questions will be created by individual pupils.

Is there anything you dislike about school? If so, what is it?

_____

What are you good at?

_____

What do you need more help with?

_____

What do you hope to achieve at school this year?

_____

Now complete the list below. Write the name of your favourite subject at the top. By the time you get to the bottom you will be left with your least favourite subject.

The pupils will make their own

choices to fill in the chart.

_____

_____

_____

_____

_____

_____

_____

_____

Subject Word Bank

Design Technology
Art PE RE Numeracy
Literacy   Science
History   Geography
Information Technology

Name: Date:

Cities and Countries in Europe

Here are the names of some cities in Europe.

Dublin   Madrid   Paris
Rome   Stockholm   London
Berlin

Here are the names of some countries in Europe.

Sweden   Germany   Italy
France   Republic of Ireland
United Kingdom   Spain

Can you say which country each city is in? The first one has been done for you.

Stockholm is in Sweden.

_____

_____

_____

_____

_____

This tower is very famous.
It is called the Eiffel Tower.
Which city is it in?

Paris

Cities and Countries in Europe

Here are the names of some cities in Europe.

Dublin   Madrid   Paris
Rome   Stockholm   London
Berlin

Here are the names of some countries in Europe.

Sweden   Germany   Italy
France   Republic of Ireland
United Kingdom   Spain

Can you say which country each city is in? The first one has been done for you.

Stockholm is in Sweden

Dublin is in the Republic of Ireland.

Madrid is in Spain.

Paris is in France.

Rome is in Italy.

London is in the United Kingdom.

Berlin is in Germany.

This tower is very famous.
It is called the Eiffel Tower.
Which city is it in?

Paris

Name: Date:

Map of a Garden

Fence Post

Sand Pit

Fence Panel

Tree

Patio
(made of
slabs)

House

Lawn

Washing Line

Shed

Answer these questions about the map of the garden.

Then follow the instructions to colour the map.

1. How many slabs wide is the patio?

2. How many slabs long is the patio?

3. How many slabs does the patio have altogether?

4. How many fence posts are there?

5. How many fence panels are there?

Colour the fence and the shed brown.

Colour the tree dark green.

Colour the sand pit yellow.

Colour the patio grey.

Colour the lawn light green.

Name: Date:

Map of a Garden

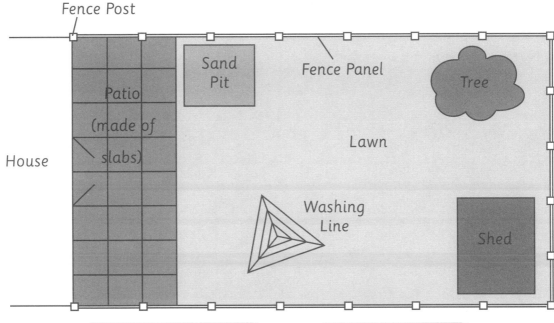

Answer these questions about the map of the garden.

Then follow the instructions to colour the map.

1. How many slabs wide is the patio? | 3 |

2. How many slabs long is the patio? | 8 |

3. How many slabs does the patio have altogether? | 24 |

4. How many fence posts are there? | 20 |

5. How many fence panels are there? | 19 |

Colour the fence and the shed brown.
Colour the tree dark green.
Colour the sand pit yellow.
Colour the patio grey.
Colour the lawn light green.

Homework Today

Name: Date:

The View from the Window

This is the view from my window.

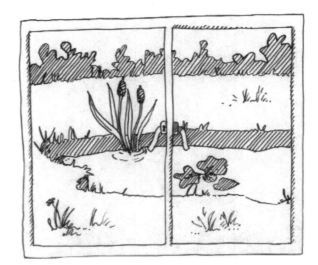

Describe the view from <u>your</u> window:

1. What buildings can you see?

_____

_____

_____

2. What can you see that is growing?

_____

_____

_____

3. What can you see that is moving?

_____

_____

_____

4. Do you like your view? Explain why.

_____

_____

_____

Name: Date:

The View from the Window

This is the view from my window.

Describe the view from <u>your</u> window:

1. What buildings can you see?

These answers will be individual to the pupil and will depend on their location.

2. What can you see that is growing?

3. What can you see that is moving?

4. Do you like your view? Explain why.

Number 45

Homework Today

Name: Date:

Materials

glass
metal
wood

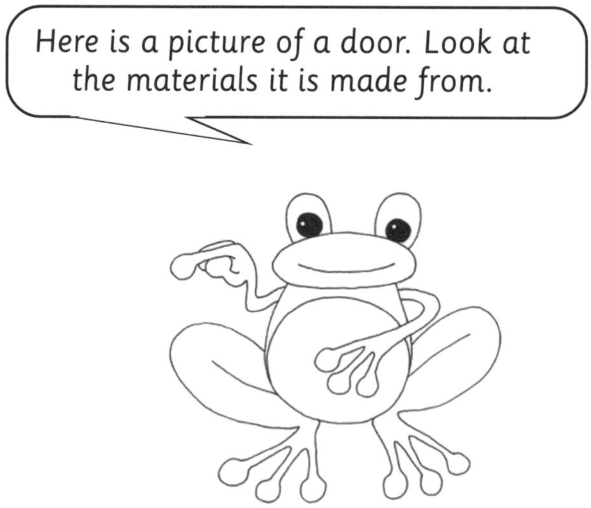

Here is a picture of a door. Look at the materials it is made from.

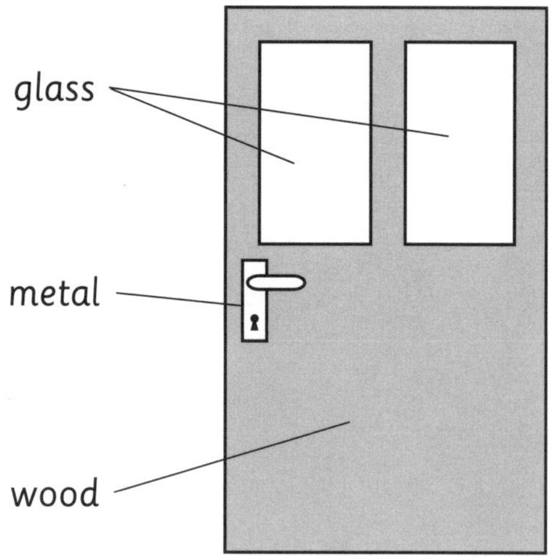

Look carefully around the room. There are lots of things in the room; what are they all made of? Make lists in the boxes:

Things made of wood

Things made of metal

Things made of plastic

Things made of other materials

Name: Date:

Materials

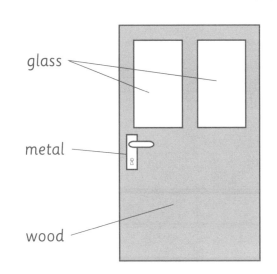

glass

metal

wood

Here is a picture of a door. Look at the materials it is made from.

Look carefully around the room. There are lots of things in the room; what are they all made of? Make lists in the boxes:

Things made of wood
table
chair
cupboard
window sill
picture frame
… and many other
possible answers.

Things made of metal
knife
fork
spoon
keys
pins
… and many other
possible answers.

Things made of plastic
telephone
light switch
CD case
pen
pencil case
… and many other
possible answers.

Things made of other materials
light bulb
carpet
plant pot
vase
… and many other
possible answers.

Name: Date:

Opaque, Transparent and Translucent

If I hold a book in front of a light bulb, I can't see the light bulb.

You can't see through a book. The book is opaque.

If I hold a glass in front of a light bulb, I can see the light bulb clearly.

You can see through a glass. The glass is transparent.

If I hold my shirt in front of a light bulb, I can see the light bulb, but not clearly.

You can see through thin cotton material. The shirt is translucent.

Turn the light on, then try holding some things in front of it. Be careful if you are using glass as it can cut you. Write your results below.

Opaque things	Transparent things	Translucent things
_____	_____	_____
_____	_____	_____
_____	_____	_____
_____	_____	_____
_____	_____	_____
_____	_____	_____
_____	_____	_____
_____	_____	_____

Name: Date:

Opaque, Transparent and Translucent

If I hold a book in front of a light bulb, I can't see the light bulb.

You can't see through a book. The book is opaque.

If I hold a glass in front of a light bulb, I can see the light bulb clearly.

You can see through a glass. The glass is transparent.

If I hold my shirt in front of a light bulb, I can see the light bulb, but not clearly.

You can see through thin cotton material. The shirt is translucent.

Turn the light on, then try holding some things in front of it. Be careful if you are using glass as it can cut you. Write your results below.

Opaque things	Transparent things	Translucent things

Children should be able to find lots of items about the home to enter in the 'opaque' and 'transparent' lists. It may be harder for them to find items to list under 'translucent' and will need some ideas given to them before they start the task.

Name: Date:

Properties of Materials

Some materials are soft and some are hard.

Some materials are stiff and some are bendy. We say that bendy things are flexible.

WORD BANK

hard   soft   stiff   flexible   transparent   strong

brittle (breaks easily)   opaque (can't see through it)

shiny   rough   smooth   dull (not shiny)

Choose from the word bank to describe each of the objects:

a wooden chair

a window pane

a dinner plate

a pullover

Homework Today   Answer Sheet

Name: Date:

Properties of Materials

Some materials are soft and some are hard.

Some materials are stiff and some are bendy. We say that bendy things are flexible.

WORD BANK

hard   soft   stiff   flexible   transparent   strong

brittle (breaks easily)   opaque (can't see through it)

shiny   rough   smooth   dull (not shiny)

Choose from the word bank to describe each of the objects:

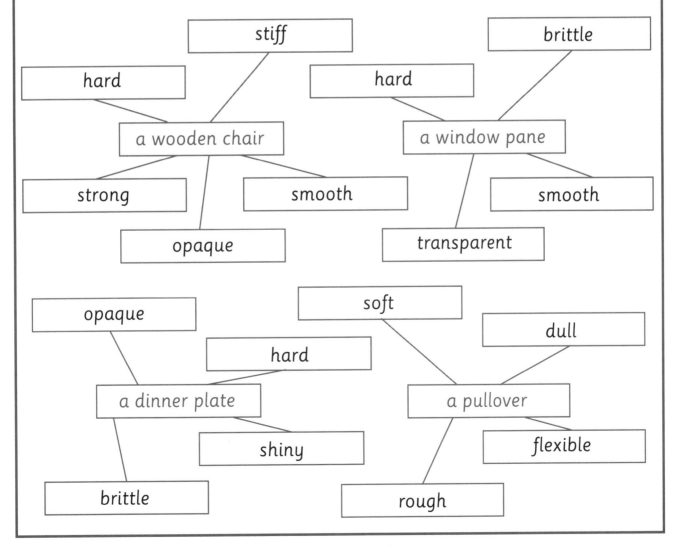

Name: Date:

Our Teeth

We have different types of teeth in our mouth. Look at your teeth in a mirror.

Incisors are at the front of your mouth. They are used for cutting food.

Canines are near the front. They are used for tearing food.

Molars are near the back. They are used for chewing food.

Humans have two sets of teeth: milk teeth, which grow when we are young, and adult teeth. After a few years the milk teeth become wobbly then fall out one by one. Adult teeth grow in their place. If the adult teeth fall out we will not grow new teeth so we must look after them.

Answer these questions:

1. What are the names of the three types of teeth?

| incisors | canines | Molars |

2. What special job do molars do?

They are used for chewing teeth

3. Why should we look after our teeth?

4. How can we look after our teeth?

Our Teeth

We have different types of teeth in our mouth. Look at your teeth in a mirror.

Incisors are at the front of your mouth. They are used for cutting food.

Canines are near the front. They are used for tearing food.

Molars are near the back. They are used for chewing food.

Humans have two sets of teeth: milk teeth, which grow when we are young, and adult teeth. After a few years the milk teeth become wobbly then fall out one by one. Adult teeth grow in their place. If the adult teeth fall out we will not grow new teeth so we must look after them.

Answer these questions:

1. What are the names of the three types of teeth?

| canine | molar | incisor |

2. What special job do incisors do?

Incisors are used to cut food.

3. Why should we look after our teeth?

After our milk teeth, these are our only set. They will not grow back if they fall out or have to be removed.

4. How can we look after our teeth?

We can look after our teeth by brushing our teeth regularly, and by eating the right foods.

Food

In the word bank, we have written the names of some different foods.

WORD BANK

chicken   salmon   orange

banana   cabbage   cod   lamb

apple   tuna   plum   lettuce

beef   pork   haddock

carrot   peas

Write the foods in the correct sets below.
Try to think of two extra ones for each set.

MEAT

chicken
Lamb
beef
Pork

FISH

Salmon
cod
tuna
haddock
b....
haddock

FRUIT

Apples
orange
banana
Plum

VEGETABLES

Lettuce
Cabbage
Peas
carrot

Write down what you have eaten today.

Apple, orange Sandwitch,
grapes, Mash, sasiges, frute
Flat Jack, banana cake, banana
Lof, vitimin

Name: Date:

Food

In the word bank, we have written the names of some different foods.

WORD BANK

chicken   salmon   orange

banana   cabbage   cod   lamb

apple   tuna   plum   lettuce

beef   pork   haddock

carrot   peas

Write the foods in the correct sets below. Try to think of two extra ones for each set.

MEAT	FISH	FRUIT
chicken	salmon	orange
lamb	cod	banana
beef	tuna	apple
pork	haddock	plum

Write down what you have eaten today.

VEGETABLES

cabbage

lettuce

carrots

peas

This part to be individual to each pupil

Fruit and Vegetables

Look for the names of fruit and
vegetables in the word-search.

When you find them, write them in
the fruit list or the vegetable list.

z	s	w	e	d	e	q	r	x	b	k	j	f
v	q	q	c	k	x	v	h	z	e	p	q	o
w	k	j	a	z	p	l	u	m	a	e	z	r
z	v	x	b	k	v	q	b	a	n	a	n	a
j	k	f	b	j	f	k	a	k	s	s	z	n
s	t	r	a	w	b	e	r	r	y	x	v	g
v	u	z	g	p	z	v	b	f	j	k	q	e
a	r	b	e	c	p	d	e	f	g	h	i	j
k	n	l	x	v	m	l	n	o	k	z	p	q
r	i	s	z	k	t	u	e	v	f	w	q	x
y	p	a	m	r	j	s	c	a	r	r	o	t

FRUIT LIST

Apple

Plum

banana

Strawberry

orange

VEGETABLE LIST

Peas

Swede

carrot

cabbage

Name: Date:

Fruit and Vegetables

Look for the names of fruit and vegetables in the word-search.

When you find them, write them in the fruit list or the vegetable list.

z	s	w	e	d	e	q	r	x	b	k	j	f
v	q	q	c	k	x	v	h	z	e	p	q	o
w	k	j	a	z	p	l	u	m	a	e	z	r
z	v	x	b	k	v	q	b	a	n	a	n	a
j	k	f	b	j	f	k	a	k	s	s	z	n
s	t	r	a	w	b	e	r	r	y	x	v	g
v	u	z	g	p	z	v	b	f	j	k	q	e
a	r	b	e	c	p	d	e	f	g	h	i	j
k	n	l	x	v	m	l	n	o	k	z	p	q
r	i	s	z	k	t	u	e	v	f	w	q	x
y	p	a	m	r	j	s	c	a	r	r	o	t

FRUIT LIST

rhubarb

apple

orange

banana

strawberry

plum

VEGETABLE LIST

carrot

swede

turnip

peas

beans

cabbage

HOMEWORK TODAY *for ages 7-8*
Individual Record Sheet

Name: Haidee	Sheet	Date completed	Comment by parent / pupil / teacher.
Fast Addition	1		
Number Spellings	2		
More Number Spellings	3		
Odds and Evens	4		
Words and Numbers	5		
Additions to 20	6		
Subtractions within 20	7		
Multiplication Tables	8		
Multiplication and Division	9		
Reading Scales	10		
A Measuring Jug	11		
Clocks	12		
Shapes	13		
Squares on a Grid	14		
The Compass	15		
Following Directions	16		
Pond Survey	17		
Adjectives	18		
Verbs	19		
More Verbs	20		
Spelling	21		
Technical Vocabulary	22		
Synonyms	23		
Antonyms and Compound Words	24		
Silent Letters	25		
Contractions	26		
Common Prefixes	27		
Comprehension	28		
Capital Letters	29		
Commas	30		
Speech Marks	31		
Punctuation	32		
World Religions	33		
Hinduism	34		
Christianity Crossword	35		
Religious Celebrations	36		
Time Line	37		
The Vikings	38		
Musical Instruments	39		
Musical Terms	40		
School	41		
Cities and Countries in Europe	42		
Map of a Garden	43		
The View from the Window	44		
Materials	45		
Opaque, Transparent and Translucent	46		
Properties of Materials	47		
Our Teeth	48		
Food	49		
Fruit and Vegetables	50		